2500 words
Level 6

水浒传

Outlaws of the Marsh (Abridged)

[明] 施耐庵 原著
马娴 李梓萌 改编
薛彧威 翻译

MP3
Download Online

Sinolingua
华语教学出版社

First Edition   2017
Second Printing   2020

ISBN 978-7-5138-1322-8
Copyright 2017 by Sinolingua Co., Ltd
Published by Sinolingua Co., Ltd
24 Baiwanzhuang Street, Beijing 100037, China
Tel: (86) 10-68320585   68997826
Fax: (86) 10-68997826   68326333
http://www.sinolingua.com.cn
E-mail: hyjx@sinolingua.com.cn
Facebook: www.facebook.com/sinolingua
Printed by Beijing Jinghua Hucais Printing Co., Ltd

Printed in the People's Republic of China

编者的话

对于广大汉语学习者来说，要想快速提高汉语水平，扩大阅读量是很有必要的。"彩虹桥"汉语分级读物为汉语学习者提供了一系列有趣、有用的汉语阅读材料。本系列读物按照词汇量进行分级，力求用限定的词汇讲述精彩的故事。本套读物主要有以下特点：

一、分级精准，循序渐进。我们参考"新汉语水平考试（HSK）词汇表"（2012 年修订版）、《汉语国际教育用音节汉字词汇等级划分（国家标准）》和《常用汉语 1500 高频词语表》等词汇分级标准，结合《欧洲语言教学与评估框架性共同标准》（CEFR），设计了一套适合汉语学习者的"彩虹桥"词汇分级标准。本系列读物分为 7 个级别（入门级*、1 级、2 级、3 级、4 级、5 级、6 级），供不同水平的汉语学习者选择，每个级别故事的生词数量不超过本级别对应词汇量的 20%。随着级别的升高，故事的篇幅逐渐加长。本系列读物与 HSK、CEFR 的对应级别，各级词汇量以及每本书的字数详见下表。

---

*　入门级（Starter）在封底用 S 标识。

级别	入门级	1级	2级	3级	4级	5级	6级
对应级别	HSK1 CEFR A1	HSK1-2 CEFR A1-A2	HSK2-3 CEFR A2-B1	HSK3 CEFR A2-B1	HSK3-4 CEFR B1	HSK4 CEFR B1-B2	HSK5 CEFR B2-C1
词汇量	150	300	500	750	1 000	1 500	2 500
字数	1 000	2 500	5 000	7 500	10 000	15 000	25 000

二、**故事精彩，题材多样**。本套读物选材的标准就是"精彩"，所选的故事要么曲折离奇，要么感人至深，对读者构成奇妙的吸引力。选题广泛取材于中国的神话传说、民间故事、文学名著、名人传记和历史故事等，让汉语学习者在阅读中潜移默化地了解中国的文化和历史。

三、**结构合理，实用性强**。"彩虹桥"系列读物的每一本书中，除了中文故事正文之外，都配有主要人物的中英文介绍、生词英文注释及例句、故事正文的英文翻译、练习题和生词表，方便读者阅读和理解故事内容，提升汉语阅读能力。练习题主要采用客观题，题型多样，难度适中，并附有参考答案，既可供汉语教师在课堂上教学使用，又可供汉语学习者进行自我水平检测。

如果您对本系列读物有什么想法，比如推荐精彩故事、提出改进意见等，请发邮件到 liuxiaolin@sinolingua. com.cn，与我们交流探讨。也可以关注我们的微信公众号 CHQRainbowBridge，随时与我们交流互动。同时，微信公众号会不定期发布有关"彩虹桥"的出版信息，以及汉语阅读、中国文化小知识等。

韩　颖　刘小琳

Preface

For students who study Chinese as a foreign language, it's crucial for them to enlarge the scope of their reading to improve their comprehension skills. The "Rainbow Bridge" Graded Chinese Reader series is designed to provide a collection of interesting and useful Chinese reading materials. This series grades each volume by its vocabulary level and brings the learners into every scene through vivid storytelling. The series has the following features:

I. A gradual approach by grading the volumes based on vocabulary levels. We have consulted the New HSK Vocabulary (2012 Revised Edition), the *Graded Chinese Syllables, Characters and Words for the Application of Teaching Chinese to the Speakers of Other Languages (National Standard)* and the 1,500 Commonly Used High Frequency Chinese Vocabulary, along with the Common European Framework of Reference for Languages (CEFR) to design the "Rainbow Bridge" vocabulary grading standard. The series is divided into seven levels (Starter*, Level 1, Level 2, Level 3, Level 4, Level 5 and Level 6) for students at different stages in their Chinese education to choose from. For each level, new words are no more than 20% of the vocabulary amount as specified in the corresponding HSK and CEFR levels. As the levels progress, the passage length will in turn increase. The following table indicates the corresponding "Rainbow Bridge" level, HSK and CEFR levels, the vocabulary amount, and number of characters.

---

*   Represented by "S" on the back cover.

Level	Starter	1	2	3	4	5	6
HSK/ CEFR Level	HSK1 CEFR A1	HSK1-2 CEFR A1-A2	HSK2-3 CEFR A2-B1	HSK3 CEFR A2-B1	HSK3-4 CEFR B1	HSK4 CEFR B1-B2	HSK5 CEFR B2-C1
Vocabulary	150	300	500	750	1,000	1,500	2,500
Characters	1,000	2,500	5,000	7,500	10,000	15,000	25,000

II. Intriguing stories on various themes. The series features engaging stories known for their twists and turns as well as deeply touching plots. The readers will find it a joyful experience to read the stories. The topics are selected from Chinese mythology, legends, folklore, literary classics, biographies of renowned people and historical tales. Such wide-ranging topics exert an invisible, yet formative, influence on readers' understanding of Chinese culture and history.

III. Reasonably structured and easy to use. For each volume of the "Rainbow Bridge" series, apart from a Chinese story, we also provide an introduction to the main characters in Chinese and English, new words with English explanations and sample sentences, and an English translation of the story, followed by comprehension exercises and a vocabulary list to help users read and understand the story and improve their Chinese reading skills. The exercises are mainly presented as objective questions that take on various forms with moderate difficulty. Moreover, keys to the exercises are also provided. The series can be used by teachers in class or by students for self-study.

If you have any questions, comments or suggestions about the series, please email us at liuxiaolin@sinolingua.com.cn. You can also exchange ideas with us via our WeChat account: CHQRainbowBridge. This account will provide updates on the series along with Chinese reading materials and cultural tips.

Han Ying and Liu Xiaolin

目　录
Contents

VII

1. 鲁达打死镇关西

主要人物和地点：
Main Characters and Places

鲁达（Lǔ Dá）：渭州提辖（相当于地方政府的警察小头目），后出家当和尚，又被称为花和尚鲁智深，梁山一百零八将之一。

Lu Da: The head of the police department of Weizhou city who later became a monk and received the name Zhishen. He was one of the 108 generals of Mount Liangshan.

镇关西（Zhènguānxī）：郑屠的绰号，一个屠夫。

Zhenguanxi: The nickname of Butcher Zheng.

金翠莲（Jīn Cuìlián）：从外地到渭州找亲戚的一个漂亮姑娘。

Jin Cuilian: A beautiful girl who came to Weizhou to look for her relatives.

渭州（Wèizhōu）：中国古代的地名，部分位于今甘肃省境内，部分位于今宁夏回族自治区内。

Weizhou: A place in ancient China located in present-day Gansu Province and Ningxia Hui Autonomous Region.

1

渭州有一个人叫鲁达，他长得又高又胖，非常喜欢帮助别人，但是遇到事情的时候容易冲动①。

有一天②，鲁达和朋友正在酒馆③喝酒④，忽然听到有人在哭。

鲁达生气地问店小二⑤："谁在打扰我们喝酒。"店小二就把正在哭的一个姑娘和一个老头叫到鲁达旁边。

鲁达问这两个人："你们为什么哭？"

姑娘哭着说："我叫金翠莲，和父亲一起来渭州找亲戚。渭州有个外号叫镇关西的人，他强迫⑥我给他做小老婆[1]，并且答应给我父亲一些钱。我刚嫁到

① 冲动 (chōngdòng) adj. impetuous
e.g., 不要冲动，应该冷静地解决问题。

② 天 (tiān) n. day
e.g., 我们哪天去看电影吧？

③ 酒馆 (jiǔguǎn) n. pub
e.g., 我们明天在这家酒馆有一个聚会。

④ 酒 (jiǔ) n. alcohol, liquor
e.g., 我们去酒吧喝酒。

⑤ 店小二 (diàn-xiǎo'èr) n. waiter
e.g., 店小二，上茶！

⑥ 强迫 (qiǎngpò) v. force, compel
e.g., 你不能强迫我做任何事情。

2

① 才 (cái) *adv.* only when
e.g., 我昨天晚上十二点才睡觉。

② 肉 (ròu) *n.* meat
e.g., 你不能只吃肉不吃蔬菜。

③ 斤 (jīn) *m.w. jin,* a unit for measuring weight which equals 0.5 kg
e.g., 苹果五块钱一斤。

④ 肉馅 (ròuxiàn) *n.* minced meat stuffing
e.g., 饺子只有肉馅的才好吃。

⑤ 肥 (féi) *adj.* fat
e.g., 我想减肥，所以不能吃肥肉。

他家，就被他老婆赶出来了。我父亲没有拿到一分钱，现在镇关西却让我们把钱还给他。我们没有钱给他，所以才①在酒馆里哭。"

鲁达听了，生气地对姑娘说："你们不要害怕，我给你们一些钱，你们赶紧离开渭州。我去教训镇关西！"

鲁达送走这两个人后就去找镇关西。

镇关西是一个杀猪的，在家里卖猪肉②。他看见鲁达来了，就问："您要买什么？"

鲁达说："你亲自给我切十斤③瘦的肉馅④，不能带一点儿肥⑤的；再切十斤肥的肉馅，不能带一点儿瘦的。"

镇关西忙了一个上午，才把肉馅切好，包起来递给鲁达。

鲁达又说："我还要十斤脆骨①，脆骨上不能有一点儿肉。"

镇关西不高兴地说："你是来捉弄②我的吧！"

鲁达把肉馅往镇关西脸上一扔，说："我今天就是来捉弄你的！"

镇关西再也忍不住了，他愤怒地拿着刀要砍鲁达。

鲁达一脚把镇关西踢③倒，一边打一边骂："让你骗金翠莲！"

镇关西哭着求④鲁达放了他。鲁达假装没有听到，

4

① 脆骨 (cuìgǔ) *n.* gristle
e.g., 我喜欢吃油炸脆骨，很香。

② 捉弄 (zhuōnòng) *v.* make a fool of sb.
e.g., 你别捉弄人，我不会上当的。

③ 踢 (tī) *v.* kick
e.g., 用脚踢人是不对的。

④ 求 (qiú) *v.* beg
e.g., 他哭着求我给他一次机会。

继续使劲儿打他。过了一会儿，<u>镇关西</u>就不再说话了。

<u>鲁达</u>想："糟糕，<u>镇关西</u>不会死了吧？"他害怕被抓，就故意生气地对<u>镇关西</u>说："你不要装死了，以后①再教训你。"然后就赶紧逃走了。

① 以后 (yǐhòu) *n.* later, afterwards e.g., 我以后想当一个作家。

[1] 小老婆（xiǎolǎopo）concubine
中国古代男子在正妻以外娶的女子。
(In ancient china) A woman who lives with a man, often in addition to his wife, but who is socially less important.

6

思考题：
Answer the following questions according to the story.

1. 鲁达有什么缺点？
2. 金翠莲为什么哭？
3. 鲁达是怎么捉弄镇关西的？

2. 鲁智深大闹五台山

主要人物和地点：
Main Characters and Places

鲁智深（Lǔ Zhìshēn）：鲁达在做和尚之后取的法名叫"智深"，后常被人称为"鲁智深"。

Lu Zhishen: Religious name of Lu Da after he became a monk.

五台山（Wǔtái Shān）：五台山是中国的一座名山，位于山西省东北部，与浙江普陀山、四川峨眉山、安徽九华山并称为"中国佛教四大名山"，山上有很多佛教寺庙。

Mount Wutai: A famous mountain in China located in the northeast part of Shanxi Province. Mount Wutai (Shanxi), Mount Putuo (Zhejiang), Mount Emei (Sichuan) and Mount Jiuhua (Anhui) are collectively known as the "Four Great Buddhist Mountains of China", on which there are many Buddhist monasteries and temples.

东京（Dōngjīng）：中国古代的地方行政区划，是北宋的首都，位于今河南省开封市。

Dongjing: Located at present-day Kaifeng City in Henan Province, Dongjing was an administrative unit in ancient China. It was the capital city of the Northern Song Dynasty (960-1127).

相国寺（Xiàngguó Sì）：相国寺是中国著名的佛教寺院。位于北宋的都城东京（即今开封市）中心。

Xiangguo Temple: A renowned Buddhist monastery in China, which was located at downtown Dongjing (present-day Kaifeng), capital city of the Northern Song Dynasty.

鲁达杀死镇关西以后，躲到五台山当了和尚[1]，法名[2]叫"智深"。可是，和尚不能喝酒，不能吃肉，鲁智深根本受不了。

有一天，鲁智深想买酒，可是卖酒的人说："和尚不能喝酒，我不能卖给你。"

鲁智深生气地把酒抢过来，"咕噜噜①"地喝起来。喝完酒，他对卖酒的人说："明天到寺庙[3]里来拿钱。"

鲁智深喝醉了，摇摇晃晃②地回寺庙。两个和尚看见了，生气地对他说："你是和尚，怎么能喝酒呢？"

这两个和尚叫来了二十多个人，想把鲁智深

① 咕噜噜 (gūlūlū)
onom. rumble, roll
e.g., 他肯定饿了，肚子咕噜噜在叫。

② 摇摇晃晃
(yáoyáohuànghuàng)
v. stumble one's way
e.g., 他喝醉了，摇摇晃晃地走回家。

8

抓起来。鲁智深拿起一根木棒①，大叫了一声②，大家吓得都往后面退。

长老⁴赶紧过来阻止："鲁智深，快把木棒放下。"长老批评了鲁智深，并且反复告诉他不可以再喝酒、打人。

鲁智深很尊敬长老，就放下木棒，痛快地答应了长老的要求。

过了一段时间，鲁智深来到一个铁匠铺⁵，让铁匠给他做一个一百多斤的禅杖⁶。

离开铁匠铺以后，鲁智深又到一个酒馆喝酒吃肉。老板看见鲁智深是和尚，就故意对他说："没有肉了。"

鲁智深不相信，就自

① 木棒 (mùbàng) *n.*
wooden club
e.g., 你为什么拿着木棒?

② 声 (shēng) *n.*
sound, voice
e.g., 他高兴得大叫了一声。

① 第(dì) *pref.* (marker of ordinal numerals) e.g., 这是我们第一次坐飞机。

己到厨房里找到肉和酒，开心地吃了起来。

酒喝完了，<u>鲁智深</u>把剩的肉包好，对老板说："明天我还要来吃。"老板无奈地答应了。

<u>鲁智深</u>回到庙里，突然感觉胃里难受，把吃的东西都吐了。和尚们看见<u>鲁智深</u>吐的东西里有肉，而且他还喝了酒，十分生气，忍不住和<u>鲁智深</u>打了起来。一直等到长老来了，大家才停下来。

第①二天，长老把<u>鲁智深</u>叫来，给了<u>鲁智深</u>一些钱，对他说："你一再违反规定，我也不能留你了。我写一封信，介绍你到<u>东京</u>的<u>相国寺</u>去吧。"

鲁智深离开寺庙，来到铁匠铺，取了禅杖，向东京方向走去。

[1] 和尚（héshang）monk
出家修行的男佛教徒。
A man who converts to Buddhism to meditate on enlightenment.

[2] 法名（fǎmíng）religious name
指出家之后由师父另起的名字。
The name given by the master after one becomes a monk.

[3] 寺庙（sìmiào）temple
供奉神佛或历史上有名人物的地方，这里指的是佛教寺庙。
The place where people pay tribute to gods or well-known figures in history. Here it refers to a Buddhist temple.

[4] 长老（zhǎnglǎo）senior monk
对年纪大、有地位的和尚的尊称。
A respectful term of address for an elderly and prestigious monk.

[5] 铁匠铺（tiějiangpù）blacksmith
铁匠铺起源于中国古代，是从事制作、贩卖各种铁器的商店。铁匠铺的铁器成品包括农具、生活用品及武器。
Blacksmith can be traced back to ancient China in which various types of ironware were made and sold. The ironware pieces includes farming tools, household articles and weapons.

[6] 禅杖（chánzhàng）monk's staff
和尚使用的手杖，也可以当作武器使用。
A walking stick used by a monk that could also act as a weapon.

思考题：
Answer the following questions according to the story.

1. 鲁智深受不了寺庙的什么规矩？

2. 鲁智深是怎么大闹五台山的？

3. 鲁智深能留在五台山吗？为什么？

3．鲁智深夜闹桃花村

主要人物和地点：
Main Characters and Places

刘太公（Liú tàigōng）：桃花村村民，有个美丽的女儿。"太公"是对长者的称呼。
Squire Liu: A villager in Peach Blossom Manor who had a beautiful daughter.

周通（Zhōu Tōng）：桃花村附近的一个强盗。
Zhou Tong: A robber who operated near the Peach Blossom Manor.

李忠（Lǐ Zhōng）：桃花村附近一伙强盗的首领。
Li Zhong: The head of the burglars who operated near the Peach Blossom Manor.

桃花村（Táohuā Cūn）：一个村庄的名字。
Peach Blossom Manor: The name of a village.

鲁智深一个人去东京相国寺，走了半个多月还没到。一天晚上，他经过桃花村，就在刘太公的家里住下。

刘太公对鲁智深说："你晚上千万不要出来。"

鲁智深很奇怪地问："为什么？"

刘太公显得很愤怒："今天晚上，我的女儿要嫁人。"

鲁智深笑着问："嫁人是好事情，你为什么不高兴呢？"

刘太公说："有一个叫周通的强盗①，强迫我把女儿嫁给他。"

鲁智深说："我去劝劝周通，让他不要娶你的女儿。"

① 强盗 (qiángdào) *n.* bandit, robber
e.g., 他遇到一个强盗，把他的钱都抢走了。

① 装作 (zhuāngzuò)
v. disguise, pretend
e.g., 你不要装作不
认识我。

② 床 (chuáng) *n.*
bed
e.g., 你应该上床睡
觉了。

③ 当成 (dàngchéng)
v. take for
e.g., 我把你的弟弟
当成你了。

鲁智深准备教训一下周通。他装作①刘太公的女儿，在房间里等着周通。房间里没有灯，周通走进房间，把床②上的鲁智深当成③了刘太公的女儿，就开始摸鲁智深。突然，鲁智深打了一下周通。

周通吃惊地说："你怎么打你的丈夫？"

鲁智深一下子把周通摔倒在地上，说："让你认识一下你的老婆。"

周通急忙喊："救我！"强盗们赶紧冲进房间救人。鲁智深放下周通，拿起禅杖朝强盗打去，打跑了强盗们。周通也趁着这个机会逃走了。

刘太公哭着对鲁智深

说："你把周通打了，这些强盗肯定会杀了我们的。"

鲁智深说："你不要害怕，我能应付他们。"

过了一会儿，突然听到有人喊："强盗的首领①带着全部强盗来了。"

鲁智深说："我去看看。"说完，他拿着禅杖来到房间外。

首领骑在马上，对着房间骂："那个和尚在哪儿？赶快出来。"

鲁智深走到首领前面说："我在这里。"

首领看到鲁智深，笑了起来，对鲁智深说："您不认识我了？"

鲁智深仔细朝首领的脸看去，原来首领是他的

① 首领 (shǒulǐng) *n.*
head, leader, chief
e.g., 他是我们的首领，我们都听他的命令。

16

好朋友李忠。

李忠请鲁智深跟他回家聊天，鲁智深答应了。到了李忠家里，周通看见鲁智深，生气地对李忠说："哥哥，你怎么把这个和尚带到家里来了？"

李忠说："你知道他是谁？他就是鲁智深。"

周通很吃惊地说："原来他就是鲁智深啊，幸亏我没有被他打死。"

鲁智深在李忠家住了几天，然后就离开桃花村，继续往东京走去。

思考题：

Answer the following questions according to the story.

1. 刘太公为什么不让鲁智深晚上出来？
2. 鲁智深是怎么教训周通的？
3. 李忠和鲁智深是什么关系？

4. 鲁智深倒拔柳树

主要人物和地点：
Main Characters and Places

张三（Zhāng Sān）：住在相国寺的菜地附近的地痞。
Zhang San: A hooligan who lived nearby the vegetable plot at Xiangguo Temple.

李四（Lǐ Sì）：张三的好朋友。
Li Si: A good friend of Zhang San.

林冲（Lín Chōng）：本书中的重要人物之一，外号豹子头，本来是东京八十万禁军教头，后投靠梁山。
Lin Chong: One of the major characters in the novel. He was nicknamed 豹子头(bàozitóu), meaning the head of a leopard. He was the instructor of the 800,000 imperial guards in Dongjing. He later joined Liangshan as a last resort.

鲁智深走了八九天，终于到了相国寺。一个和尚带着鲁智深找到方丈[1]。

鲁智深把五台山长老写的信给了方丈。方丈看了信，知道了鲁智深在五台山做的事情，怕鲁智深在相国寺惹祸，不想让鲁智深住在相国寺，但又不好意思拒绝。

这时候，一个和尚对方丈说："我想起来了，咱们寺有一片菜地①。那里经常有一些人偷菜，可以让鲁智深住在那里，管理菜地。"方丈同意了。

张三和李四两个人经常在相国寺的菜地偷菜。他们商量好了，要教训一下鲁智深，让鲁智深不敢

① 菜地 (càidì) *n.* vegetable plot e.g., 他家附近有一片菜地。

① 跪 (guì) *v.* kneel
e.g., 赶快站起来，
不要跪着了。

② 粪坑 (fènkēng) *n.*
manure pit
e.g., 粪坑旁边太臭
了。

③ 扑通 (pūtōng)
onom. splash, flop
e.g., 石头"扑通"
一声掉进水里。

④ 饭 (fàn) *n.* dinner
e.g., 再等一会儿，
饭马上就做好了。

管理菜地。

一天，张三和李四带着十几个人，来到鲁智深住的地方，跪① 在粪坑② 旁边不起来。鲁智深不知道他们为什么跪下，就走过去，想把他们扶起来。

张三和李四看见鲁智深走到附近，突然一人抱住鲁智深的一条腿，想把鲁智深推下粪坑。

让人意想不到的是，鲁智深用脚一踢，就听到"扑通③ ！扑通！"两声，张三和李四滚进了粪坑。其他人都吓得跪下，不敢有任何动作。鲁智深大笑着教训了这些人一顿。

第二天，张三和李四跑来请鲁智深吃饭④ ，向鲁智深道歉。大家在一棵大柳树①下坐着吃东西、喝酒、聊天。突然，他们听到柳树上有一只乌鸦②在叫。有个人就想爬③上树赶走乌鸦。

鲁智深说："你们看我怎么把乌鸦赶走。"说完，他走到柳树下，抱住这棵树，一使劲儿，就把整棵树从地里拔④了出来。

张三和李四十分害怕，跪下说："您的力气真大呀！"

鲁智深却说："这没有什么，让你们看看我的本领。"鲁智深拿起禅杖，开始表演功夫²，大家都看呆了。

这个时候，忽然听到外面有人说："真是好本领！"

① 柳树 (liǔshù) n. willow tree
e.g., 柳树上有一只小鸟。

② 乌鸦 (wūyā) n. crow
e.g., 乌鸦的叫声很难听。

③ 爬 (pá) v. climb, crawl
e.g., 这个孩子还小，不会走路，只会爬。

④ 拔 (bá) v. pull out
e.g., 他要去医院拔牙。

鲁智深向外面一看，是一个三十四五岁的中年男人，就问张三和李四："他是什么人？"

李四说："他是八十万士兵的武术老师，叫林冲。"

鲁智深走到林冲旁边，高兴地对林冲说："我是鲁智深，小时候曾经与您的父亲见过面。"

林冲十分高兴，就叫鲁智深哥哥，两个人坐下来一起喝酒，后来成了好朋友。

[1] 方丈（fāngzhang）abbot (monk)
方丈是佛教中对大寺庙最高领导者的尊称。
A respectful form of address for the senior monk in charge of a Buddhist temple.

[2] 功夫（gōngfu）kung fu
中国传统武术，即打拳和使用刀枪剑棍等武器的技术。
Traditional Chinese martial arts which includes boxing, sword, spear and cudgel skills.

1. 方丈为什么不想让鲁智深住在相国寺？

2. 张三和李四想怎么教训鲁智深？

3. 鲁智深为什么要拔柳树？

5. 林冲错闯白虎节堂

主要人物和地点：
Main Characters and Places

高太尉（Gāo tàiwèi）：名叫高俅，北宋掌管军事的高官，官名为"太尉"。

Grand Marshal Gao: His name is Gao Qiu. He was a high-ranking official in charge of military affairs in the Northern Song Dynasty (960-1127). 太尉 is his official title.

高衙内（Gāo yánèi）：高太尉的干儿子，"衙内"指官僚子弟。

Master Gao: The adopted son of Grand Marshal Gao. 衙内 refers to children of the bureaucrats.

陆谦（Lù Qiān）：林冲的朋友，后多次设计陷害林冲。

Lu Qian: He was once a friend of Lin Chong, but later he designed several plots to frame Lin.

薛霸、董超（Xuē Bà, Dǒng Chāo）：开封府的衙役，相当于现在的警察。

Xue Ba and Dong Chao: They were the guards of the official residence of Kaifeng, equivalent to present-day policemen.

沧州（Cāngzhōu）：中国古代地名，位于今河北省境内，在北宋时是宋辽边境。

Cangzhou: A place in ancient China, now in Hebei Province. It was an area bordering the State of Liao during the Northern Song Dynasty.

① 讨好 (tǎohǎo) *v.*
curry favor with
e.g., 他想讨好我，
我才不搭理他呢。

东京有一个高衙内，到处做坏事。可是因为他干爹[1]高太尉是很大的官，所以没有人敢教训他。

有一天，高衙内遇到了林冲的妻子，觉得她长得很漂亮，就想把她抢过来。但是林冲功夫很厉害，所以高衙内也不敢轻易做什么。

林冲的朋友陆谦一直想讨好①高衙内和高太尉。他看见高衙内因为得不到林冲的妻子很不高兴，就给他想了一个主意。

几天以后，陆谦把林冲请出去吃饭，又派人去林冲家对林冲的妻子说："您的丈夫突然生病了，摔倒在地上，您赶紧去看看吧。"

　　林冲的妻子马上带着丫鬟①跑到陆谦家，却发现林冲根本不在，只有高衙内在。她急忙派丫鬟去通知林冲，林冲及时赶到，把高衙内打跑了。

　　高衙内回家以后，又失望又害怕，就生病了。

　　高太尉没有儿子，只有高衙内这么一个干儿子[2]，非常疼爱②他。现在看到高衙内的病一直不好，很着急。

　　陆谦对高太尉说："只要林冲死了，把他的妻子抢来，高衙内就能好起来。"于是高太尉和陆谦商量怎么才能杀死林冲。

　　又过了几天，林冲在

① 丫鬟 (yāhuan) n.
servant girl, maid
e.g., 这个丫鬟长得真漂亮。

② 疼爱 (téng'ài) v.
love dearly
e.g., 妈妈非常疼爱我。

① 死罪 (sǐzuì) *n.*
capital offense
e.g., 他杀了人，这
是死罪。

街上遇到一个卖刀的。林冲看那把刀是把好刀，就买下了。

第二天，有两个人来找林冲，对他说："听人说，您买了一把好刀，高太尉想看一下。"林冲只好同意了。

那两个人带着林冲来到高太尉家的一个房间，然后就离开了。

林冲觉得很奇怪，忽然看见门上有几个大字："白虎节堂³"。白虎节堂是非常重要的地方，没有高太尉的允许，别人不能进来，否则就是死罪①。

林冲吓了一跳，刚想离开，高太尉就出现了。高太尉生气地对林冲说：

① 擅自 (shànzì) *adv.*
presumptuously
e.g., 他没有告诉老师，擅自离开教室。

② 罪名 (zuìmíng) *n.*
charge, accusation
e.g., 故意杀人的罪名可不小。

③ 判 (pàn) *v.* sentence, make a ruling
e.g., 他被判了十年徒刑。

④ 衙役 (yáyì) *n.*
escorting guard
e.g., 衙役负责押送犯人。

⑤ 押送 (yāsòng) *v.*
escort
e.g., 这辆车用来给银行押送钱。

"你怎么拿着刀进白虎节堂，是不是想杀我？"

林冲解释说："是您派人叫我来的。"

高太尉说："胡说！我根本没有派人叫你。"

林冲被人抓起来，送到了官府⁴。

官府的官员很同情林冲。他们想到了一个主意：把林冲"擅自①闯进白虎节堂"罪名②的"擅自"改成"不小心"，说明林冲不是故意闯进白虎节堂的，因此没有判③林冲死罪，而是把林冲发配⁵到沧州，又派薛霸和董超两个衙役④押送⑤林冲。

[1] 干爹（gāndiē）adoptive father
中国传统文化中有认干爹的习俗，干爹是干亲的一种，指生父以外认的父亲。
It is a traditional Chinese custom to take someone as one's nominally adoptive kinsman or kinswoman. 干爹 refers to one's nominally adoptive father.

[2] 干儿子（gān'érzi）adopted son
干亲的一种，指生儿子以外认的儿子。
干儿子 refers to one's nominally adoptive son.

[3] 白虎节堂（Báihǔ Jiétáng）White Tiger Hall
白虎节堂是古代军事重地，相当于现代的军备司令部，任何人不经允许，不得携带武器进入。
An important military site in ancient China which was equivalent to a present-day military headquarters. No one was allowed to enter with weapons without special permission.

[4] 官府（guānfǔ）local government office
中国古代的地方行政机关，州、县等地方行政区域都设有官府。
The local administrative bodies in ancient China which were set up at prefecture and county levels, etc.

[5] 发配（fāpèi）banish into the services
发配是宋代的一种刑罚，先在罪犯的脸上刺字，然后送到边远地区去服劳役。
A criminal penalty in the Song Dynasty: criminals were first labeled as criminals by having insulting characters tatooed in their faces and were then banished to a remote area for penal servitude.

思考题：
Answer the following questions according to the story.

1. 高衙内为什么生病了？

2. 陆谦是真的请林冲吃饭吗？

3. 林冲为什么进了白虎节堂？

6. 鲁智深野猪林救林冲

主要人物和地点：
Main Characters and Places

野猪林（Yězhūlín）：一个经常有野兽出没的地方，十分危险，很多人在此丧生。

Wild Boar Woods: A very dangerous place as wild beasts frequented the area and claimed many lives.

林冲没被判死罪，高太尉又想了一个办法杀林冲。他派人送钱给薛霸和董超两个衙役，让他们在路上弄死林冲，薛霸和董超立刻就答应了。

一路上，薛霸和董超对林冲又打又骂，还用热水烫坏了林冲的两只脚。

晚上，他们到了野猪林。野猪林是一个很危险的地方，所以很少有人来。薛霸说："我累了，不想走了。"

董超说："我也不想走了。"

林冲听了，就靠着一棵大树坐下了，可是，薛霸和董超却拿出绳子，把

① 捆 (kǔn) *v.* tie, bind
e.g., 我们要用绳子捆书。

② 跳 (tiào) *v.* jump
e.g., 他高兴地跳了起来。

③ 马车 (mǎchē) *n.* carriage
e.g., 他家有一辆马车。

林冲捆① 了起来。

薛霸对林冲说："高太尉要杀你，我们必须照他说的做。"

就在薛霸要杀林冲的时候，从大树后面跳② 出来一个胖和尚，原来是鲁智深。他举着禅杖要杀薛霸、董超，林冲赶紧阻止，"这是高太尉的主意，他们怎么敢不听呢？还是放了他们吧！"

鲁智深拿出刀，把捆林冲的绳子弄断，然后说："我听别人说，你被押送到沧州，于是我就一直跟着你，想保护你。我猜他们会在野猪林杀你，就提前赶到这里。"

鲁智深找了一辆马车③，

让林冲坐上去休息。薛霸、董超知道这个胖和尚厉害，都不敢反对。

鲁智深保护着林冲走了十几天，林冲的脚也差不多好了。

一天，鲁智深对林冲说："快到沧州了，我就不再跟着了。我已经问了，这附近都有人住，他们俩不敢杀你，放心吧。"

鲁智深拿出一些钱给林冲，又指着一棵大树对薛霸和董超说："你们俩要是再伤害他，我就让你们和这大树一样。"说完，鲁智深举起禅杖，一下就把大树砍断了。

董超吃惊地说："这个和尚真厉害。"

林冲说："这有什么？在相国寺，他一下就把一棵柳树从地里拔出来了。"

薛霸、董超才知道，胖和尚就是相国寺的鲁智深。

思考题：

Answer the following questions according to the story.

1. 是谁命令薛霸和董超杀死林冲的？
2. 薛霸和董超想在哪里杀死林冲？
3. 哪个人突然出现，救了林冲？

7. 林冲被逼上梁山

主要人物和地点：
Main Characters and Places

梁山（Liáng Shān）：又称水泊梁山，位于今山东省梁山县境内。《水浒传》的故事就发生在这里。

Liangshan: Also known as Liangshan Marsh. It is located within present-day Liangshan County of Shandong Province, where the stories in this novel occur.

薛霸、董超押送林冲来到沧州，把林冲关进沧州的监狱①，就回去报告高太尉：他们没有杀死林冲。

高太尉又派陆谦去沧州杀林冲。

林冲到了沧州以后，监狱的官派林冲去管理沧州东边的一座草料场[1]。一个小官带着林冲来到草料场。这个时候天空开始下大雪。小官把大门的钥匙交给林冲，就离开了。

林冲一个人待在草料场，觉得很冷，就走到一个酒馆，买了几斤肉，又买了一些酒。当他回到草料场的时候，却发现大雪把他住的房子②压③倒了。雪太大了，去哪儿住呢？

① 监狱 (jiānyù) *n.*
prison, jail
e.g., 犯罪可能会被抓进监狱。

② 房子 (fángzi) *n.*
house
e.g., 这间房子是我自己盖的。

③ 压 (yā) *v.* weigh down
e.g., 你不要压着我，我难受。

① 武器 (wǔqì) *n.*
weapon
e.g., 鲁智深的武器
是禅杖。

林冲想到从酒馆回来的路上有一个寺庙，于是拿着武器① 和被子来到这个寺庙，准备在这里睡觉。

过了一会儿，林冲突然发现草料场着火了。他正想去草料场救火，忽然听到有三个人来到寺庙外。寺庙的大门被林冲用石头挡着，这三个人推不开大门，就站在寺庙外。

一个人说："谢谢你帮忙，等我回去把这件事情告诉高太尉，高太尉一定会升你的官。"

第二个人说："我爬进草料场，在四五个地方放了火，林冲一定已经死了。"

另一个人说："一会儿咱们去草料场捡几块林冲

① 仇 (chóu) *n.*
hatred, enmity
e.g., 他们两家有仇。

② 逼 (bī) *v.*
force, compel
e.g., 妈妈逼我学习跳舞。

的骨头，我带回去给高太尉看。"

林冲听得很清楚，寺庙外的三个人正是陆谦、高俅的手下和带他来草料场的小官。林冲十分生气，他想："真是幸运，要不是房子倒了，我肯定被这三个人杀死了。"

林冲悄悄把石头推开，拿着刀冲出寺庙，先杀了那个小官和高俅的手下，然后走向陆谦，一脚把陆谦踢倒。陆谦十分害怕，他对林冲大喊："不要杀我！"

林冲说："我跟你没仇①，你为什么要杀我？"

陆谦害怕地说："不是我想杀你，都是高太尉逼②

我做的啊！跟我没关系！"

林冲说："我一直把你当朋友，你却要杀我，怎么跟你没关系？"

林冲说完，一刀杀死了陆谦。

林冲知道自己杀了人，犯了死罪，所以不敢留在沧州。他听说梁山有一群强盗，就准备去梁山做强盗。

[1] 草料场（cǎoliàochǎng）fodder depot
草料场是宋代一个官府部门，掌管军队的草料储积。草料特指养马的饲料。
An official department in the Song Dynasty which was in charge of the storage of horse feed for military use.

思考题：
Answer the following questions according to the story.

1. 是谁派陆谦来沧州杀林冲的？
2. 陆谦想怎么杀死林冲？
3. 林冲为什么不敢留在沧州？

8. 杨志东京卖宝刀

主要人物和地点：
Main Characters and Places

杨志（Yáng Zhì）：北宋名将杨令公的孙子。
Yang Zhi: The grandson of the famous general Yang Ye of the
   Northern Song Dynasty.

牛二（Niú Èr）：东京的地痞，经常做坏事。
Niu Er: A hooligan in Dongjing who often committed wrongdoings.

大名府（Dàmíng Fǔ）：中国古代的地名，位于今河北省大
   名县。
Damingfu: A place name in ancient China. It was located in
   present-day Daming County, Hebei Province.

有一个叫杨志的人，功夫很厉害。他带着钱想去东京买一个官做。

杨志到了东京，几天就把钱都花完了，官还是没有做上。为了吃饭，他只好去市场卖长辈留给他的宝刀①。

在市场里，杨志拿着刀，等着人们询问价格。一个叫牛二的坏人喝醉了，摇摇晃晃地走到杨志旁边问："你的刀多少钱？"

杨志说："三千贯[1]。"

牛二说："你的刀太贵了。"

杨志说："我这把刀是最好的刀。第一，可以砍开铜钱[2]，刀不会坏；第二，把头发吹到刀上，头

① 宝刀 (bǎodāo) *n.* treasured sword e.g., 这把刀是一把宝刀，我很喜欢它。

① 摞 (luò) v. pile up
e.g., 你把这几个箱子摞起来。

② 头 (tóu) n. head
e.g., 你低一下头，小心撞到门。

发马上就断；第三，杀人的时候刀上不会有血。"

牛二拿出二十个铜钱摞①在一起，让杨志拿刀砍。杨志一刀砍下去，把二十个铜钱全部砍为两半。旁边的人都兴奋地叫起来。

牛二不高兴了，他大喊："有什么了不起的！"他又从自己的头②上拔了一把头发，让杨志用刀试试。杨志拿着头发往刀上一吹，头发就都断了。大家又兴奋地叫起来。

牛二更不高兴了。他对杨志说："我不相信杀人的时候刀上不会有血，你用这把刀杀个人给我看看。"

杨志说："我杀一条狗给你看看吧。"

① 自首 (zìshǒu) v.
give oneself up (to
the police, authority,
etc.)
e.g., 他犯了罪，主
动去找警察自首。

牛二就骂杨志："你说的是杀人的时候刀上没有血，没有说杀狗的时候刀上没有血。"

杨志不高兴地说："你要是不买刀就离开，不要打扰我卖刀。"

牛二却不答应。他对杨志说："你敢杀我吗？"

杨志十分生气，拿着刀想要离开这里。牛二拦着杨志，说："不能走，你要是有本领，就把我杀了。"说完就冲杨志打去。

杨志太生气了，就一刀把牛二杀了，然后到官府去自首①。

到了官府，杨志主动讲了事情的经过。官府的官觉得杨志很有本领，杀

的又是一个坏人，就没有
判<u>杨志</u>死罪，只把杨志发
配到<u>大名府</u>，但是那把刀
却被官府没收① 了。

① 没收 (mòshōu) v.
confiscate
e.g., 我上课玩手机，
老师把我的手机没收
了。

[1] 贯 (guàn) *guan* (a string of 1000 coins)
中国古代货币——铜钱的单位，一贯钱等于一千个铜钱。
A unit of currency for the copper coin in ancient China. One *guan* is equivalent to 1,000 copper coins.

[2] 铜钱 (tóngqián) copper coin
中国古代的铜质货币，一般为圆形，中间有方孔。
A kind of currency made of copper in ancient China. It is round- shaped with a square hole in the middle.

思考题：
Answer the following questions according to the story.

1. 杨志为什么要在东京卖刀？
2. 哪几个方面可以证明杨志的刀是最好的刀？
3. 杨志为什么没有被判死罪？

9. 晁盖抢走生辰纲

主要人物和地点：
Main Characters and Places

晁盖（Cháo Gài）：本书的主要人物之一。他是梁山好汉的首领，人称"托塔天王"。

Chao Gai: One of the main characters in the novel. He was the head of the outlaws at Liangshan Marsh, and had the nickname the "Pagoda-shifting Heavenly King".

梁中书（Liáng zhōngshū）：大名府的知府，宰相蔡京的女婿。"中书"是官名。

Grand Secretary Liang: The magistrate of Damingfu and the son-in-law of Prime Minister Cai Jing. 中书 is an official title.

蔡京（Cài Jīng）：北宋的宰相、书法家，十分有权势，以贪渎闻名。

Cai Jing: Cai Jing was the Prime Minister of the Northern Song Dynasty and also a calligrapher. He wielded great power and influence, but was infamous for corruption and malfeasance.

吴用（Wú Yòng）：跟随晁盖加入梁山，梁山好汉的军师，满腹经纶，足智多谋，人称"智多星"。

Wu Yong: Joined Liangshan after robbing the birthday gift convoy with Chao Gai, he served as the military adviser of Liangshan. He was profoundly learned as a master of strategy and was hence nicknamed the "Resourceful Star".

公孙胜（Gōngsūn Shèng）：一个道士，武艺高强，跟随晁盖加入梁山，绰号"入云龙"。

Gongsun Sheng: A Taoist priest with great martial arts skills.

He joined Liangshan with Chao Gai. "Dragon in the Clouds" was his nickname.

刘唐（Liú Táng）：擅长的武器是大刀，武艺过人，有情有义，但有些鲁莽冲动。跟随晁盖加入梁山，人称"赤发鬼"。

Liu Tang: A faithful yet reckless figure in the novel. Possessed of outstanding martial arts skills, he was adept at using the broadsword. He joined Liangshan with Chao Gai. "Red Haired Devil" was his nickname.

阮小二、阮小五、阮小七（Ruǎn Xiǎo'èr、Ruǎn Xiǎowǔ、Ruǎn Xiǎoqī）：三人是亲兄弟，居住在梁山旁边的石碣村，武艺出众，很讲义气，后来跟随晁盖加入梁山。

Ruan Xiao'er, Ruan Xiaowu and Ruan Xiaoqi: They were brothers born of the same parents and lived together in Shijie Village near Liangshan. Possessed of outstanding martial arts skills, the three brothers cherished brotherhood loyalty. They joined Liangshan with Chao Gai.

白胜（Bái Shèng）：因与晁盖等人一起抢劫生辰纲而被抓，后从监狱逃出，加入梁山。

Bai Sheng: He was captured when he joined Chao Gai and his companions and robbed the birthday gift convoy. Then he managed to escape from the jail and joined Liangshan.

郓城县（Yùnchéng Xiàn）：中国古代的地名，位于今山东省西南部。郓城县是水浒故事的发祥地，晁盖等人的家就在郓城县。

Yuncheng County: A place name in ancient China. Situated in the southwest of present-day Shandong Province, Yuncheng County was the matrix of the stories in *Outlaws of the Marsh* and the home of Chao Gai and some of his companions.

① 岳父 (yuèfù)
*n.*father-in-law
e.g., 妻子的父亲就
是岳父。

② 贪官 (tānguān) *n.*
corrupt official
e.g., 贪官应该受到
惩罚。

　　杨志被发配到大名府。因为杨志的功夫很厉害，所以大名府的知府[1]梁中书派他送生辰纲[2]到东京，给他的岳父①蔡京作生日礼物。

　　梁中书和蔡京都是贪官②。郓城县的晁盖、吴用、公孙胜、刘唐、阮小二、阮小五、阮小七这七个人知道了这个消息。他们想为老百姓出口气，把生辰纲抢走。

　　杨志带着几个士兵出发了。一天，天气非常热，士兵们又累又热。他们把东西扔到地上，都跑到树下休息。

　　这个时候，一个卖酒的农民朝他们走来。士兵们都想买一点儿酒喝。可是杨志却阻止说："不能买。万一他的酒里放了迷药[3]怎么办？"

农民生气地说："我又不想把酒卖给你，你胡说什么！"

过了一会儿，又来了七个推着车①卖枣②的人，他们看见有人在卖酒，就赶紧过来说："给我们一桶③酒。"

农民指着杨志说："他说我的酒有迷药，我不卖了。"

卖枣的人说："他说有迷药，我们又没有说。"

农民说："好吧，就卖给你们一桶。"

喝完了一桶酒，卖枣的七个人还想喝。趁农民不注意的时候，其中一个卖枣的人打开第二桶酒，拿起碗就喝。农民看见了，赶紧抢了回来，把酒倒回了桶里。

士兵们更想喝酒了，他

① 车 (chē) *n.* cart
e.g., 车上装的都是水果。

② 枣 (zǎo) *n.* jujube
e.g., 这里的枣又大又甜。

③ 桶 (tǒng) *n.* barrel
e.g., 这个桶可以装水。

54

们对<u>杨志</u>说："我们也买一桶吧。"

其实<u>杨志</u>也渴了。他想："卖枣的人喝了一桶，另外一桶他们也喝了一些，说明酒里没有迷药。"于是，<u>杨志</u>就答应了士兵们的请求。农民拿到钱就走了。

<u>杨志</u>和士兵们把那桶酒喝完了。过了一会儿，<u>杨志</u>觉得头晕。那七个卖枣的人笑着说："倒了，倒了。"

<u>杨志</u>很吃惊，想站起来，可是却没有力气。他想叫士兵，可是发现士兵们已经倒在地上了。

原来，这些卖枣的人就是<u>晁盖</u>、<u>吴用</u>、<u>公孙胜</u>、<u>刘唐</u>、<u>阮小二</u>、<u>阮小五</u>、<u>阮小七</u>这七个人，卖酒的

农民是<u>白胜</u>。迷药是<u>刘唐</u>打开第二桶酒喝了以后才放进去的。

　　<u>晁盖</u>他们先把车上的枣扔到地上，然后把生辰纲放到车里，高兴地推着车走了。

[1] 知府（zhīfǔ）magistrate of a prefecture
知府是一个官名，北宋时地方行政区域"府"的最高长官。
It was an official title during China's Northern Song Dynasty. The official was the highest-ranking one of 府, a local administrative unit.

[2] 生辰纲（Shēngchéngāng）birthday gift convoy
生辰纲指成批运送的生日礼物。"生辰"就是生日的意思，"纲"指的是成批运输货物的组织。
Birthday gifts which are transported in batches. 生辰 means birthday, and 纲 refers to an organization that transports certain goods in large quantities under a convoy.

[3] 迷药（míyào）knockout drug
迷药是一种可以迅速导致人昏睡的药物，人服用过迷药后，经过一段时间才能苏醒。
A type of drug that can make people fall asleep quickly. It would take quite a while for people to regain consciousness after taking this drug.

1. 晁盖、吴用、公孙胜、刘唐、阮小二、阮小五、阮小七
   这七个人为什么抢走生辰纲？
2. 卖酒的人和卖枣的人认识吗？
3. 迷药是什么时候放进酒里的？

10. 鲁智深、杨志夺二龙山

主要人物和地点：
Main Characters and Places

曹正（Cáo Zhèng）：杨志的好朋友，后随杨志、鲁智深一起加入梁山。

Cao Zheng: A good friend of Yang Zhi. He later joined Liangshan along with Yang and Lu zhishen.

邓龙（Dèng Lóng）：二龙山的强盗首领，后被鲁智深杀死。

Deng Long: The ringleader on Erlong Mountainwho was later killed by Lu Zhishen.

二龙山（Èrlóng Shān）：本书中的一个地名。

Erlong Mountain: A place name in the novel.

杨志丢了生辰纲，他害怕梁中书生气，不敢再回大名府，准备去梁山做强盗。

在去梁山的路上，杨志遇到了好朋友曹正。

杨志告诉了曹正自己的打算，曹正听后说："这附近有一座二龙山，山上有一群强盗，首领叫邓龙。你不如去二龙山，把邓龙赶走，自己做二龙山的主人。"

杨志说："这个主意很好。"

第二天早上，杨志就出发去二龙山了。他刚走到一片树林①，就看见一个胖和尚正坐在大树下休息。

胖和尚看见杨志，不

① 树林 (shùlín) n. woods, forest e.g., 这片树林里生长着很多大树。

客气地问："我叫<u>鲁智深</u>，你是从哪儿来的？"

<u>杨志</u>吃惊地说："你就是<u>鲁智深</u>啊！你不是在<u>相国寺</u>吗？"

<u>鲁智深</u>回答说："因为我在<u>野猪林</u>里救了<u>林冲</u>，所以<u>高太尉</u>很恨我，派人到处抓我，我只好离开<u>相国寺</u>了。"

<u>杨志</u>也跟<u>鲁智深</u>讲了自己的经历。因为两个人都觉得对方是英雄，所以他们很快成为了好朋友，并且还商量要一起去<u>二龙山</u>。

过了一天，<u>曹正</u>带了几个人来帮助<u>杨志</u>。他们想了一个办法，让<u>鲁智深</u>脱了衣服，大家用绳子把

他捆起来，然后一起往二龙山走去。

刚到二龙山，就遇到几个人，他们问曹正来干什么。

曹正说："这个和尚说要杀了邓龙首领，然后自己做二龙山的主人。我趁他喝醉的时候，把他捆了起来，要交给邓龙首领。"那几个人听了，就带曹正他们去见①邓龙。

邓龙看见鲁智深，生气地骂："你这个臭和尚，竟然想杀了我！"

忽然，鲁智深把绳子弄断，拿起禅杖朝他打过去。邓龙还没有明白发生了什么事情，就被鲁智深打死了。

① 见 (jiàn) *v.* meet, see

曹正对其他的人喊："要是不想死，就听我们的命令。"二龙山的人看见邓龙已经死了，就都扔下了武器。

从此，杨志和鲁智深做了二龙山的主人。

思考题：
Answer the following questions according to the story.

1. 杨志为什么要去做强盗？
2. 鲁智深为什么离开相国寺？
3. 大家为什么用绳子把鲁智深捆起来？

11. 朱仝后门放晁盖

主要人物和地点：
Main Characters and Places

朱仝（Zhū Tóng）：曾经是郓城县的小官，后来加入梁山。
Zhu Tong: A low-ranking official in Yuncheng County. He joined Liangshan later.

何涛（Hé Tāo）：济州府缉捕观察（相当于今天的刑警队长）。
He Tao: Head of the criminal police force in Jizhou.

何清（Hé Qīng）：何涛的弟弟。
He Qing: The younger brother of He Tao.

宋江（Sòng Jiāng）：本书中的主要人物之一，人称"及时雨"。他原来是郓城县的一个小官，后被逼上梁山，在晁盖死后成为梁山最大的首领。
Song Jiang: One of the main characters in the novel nicknamed "Timely Rain". He used to be a low-ranking official in Yuncheng County before joining Liangshan as a last resort. After the death of Chao Gai, Song Jiang became the foremost leader.

雷横（Léi Héng）：郓城县的小官，有一身好武艺，后来加入梁山。
Lei Heng: A low-ranking official in Yuncheng County with great martial arts skills. Later, he joined Liangshan.

朱贵（Zhū Guì）：在梁山脚下开酒店，专门负责探听往来客商的消息及迎接投奔梁山的人。
Zhu Gui: He ran a pub at the foot of Mount Liangshan to probe for information about the traveling merchants and receive people who came to join the outlaws.

济州（Jìzhōu）：中国古代的地名，位于今山东省。

Jizhou: A place in ancient China situated in present-day Shandong Province.

安乐村（Ānlè Cūn）：一个村庄的名字，位于今山东省。

Anle Village: A village in the novel located in present-day Shandong Province.

跟着杨志一起送生辰纲的人回到大名府，骗梁中书说："杨志和那些强盗一起抢了生辰纲。"

梁中书告诉了他的岳父蔡京。蔡京很生气，他命令济州知府赶快把杨志和强盗抓起来。

济州知府接到蔡京的命令，马上派何涛去抓这些强盗。何涛找了几个月，却仍然不知道强盗是谁，十分着急。

这个时候，何涛的弟弟何清对他说："几天以前，我在安乐村遇到晁盖、白胜这几个人，他们拿着很重的行李箱。过了几天我就听到生辰纲被抢了。肯定是晁盖他们干的。"

何涛马上抓到了白胜。白胜十分害怕地说："不要杀我，我把知道的全部告诉你。抢生辰纲的人就是晁盖、吴用这几个人。"

晁盖的家在郓城县。何涛来到郓城县抓晁盖，遇到在官府当小官的宋江。宋江听说何涛要抓的人就是自己的好朋友晁盖后，悄悄来到晁盖的家，把事情告诉了晁盖，让晁盖赶快逃走。

何涛把抓晁盖的事情告诉了郓城县的县令[1]，县令马上派朱仝和雷横去抓晁盖。

朱仝和雷横来到晁盖家，晁盖这时还没来

得及走。朱仝认识晁盖，他不想抓晁盖，就让雷横带着人到前面的门抓人，自己在后面的门等着晁盖。

晁盖来到后面的门，朱仝看到旁边没有人，对晁盖说："你快走吧，赶紧去梁山。"

晁盖说了声"谢谢"，就往梁山逃去。

晁盖、吴用这些人逃到梁山附近，遇到阮小二、阮小五和阮小七，他们也想跟着晁盖一起去梁山。

晁盖、吴用这些人带着阮小二、阮小五和阮小七来到朱贵的酒馆。朱贵就是梁山的人，他知道晁盖这些人抢了生辰纲，觉得他们是英雄，于是带着他们上了梁山。

[1] 县令（xiànlìng）county magistrate
县令是中国古代的一个官名，是县一级行政机关的最高领导，接受知府领导。
An official title in ancient China, which was the highest rank at the county level. The county magistrate was subordinate to the prefecture magistrate.

思考题：
Answer the following questions according to the story.

1. 杨志是和晁盖一起抢的生辰纲吗？

2. 何清怎么知道晁盖、白胜这些人就是抢生辰纲的人？

3. 文中有哪些人帮助过晁盖？

12. 林冲梁山杀王伦

主要人物和地点：
Main Characters and Places

王伦（Wáng Lún）：梁山的首任首领，心胸狭窄，难以容忍
  能力比他大的人，后被林冲杀死。

Wang Lun: The first chieftain of the outlaw band on Liangshan.
  He was narrow-minded and couldn't tolerate anyone more
  competent than himself. Wang ended up being killed by Lin
  Chong.

① 句 (jù) *m.w.*
sentence
e.g., 他说得太快，
我只能记下三四句
话。

② 话 (huà) *n.* word,
talk
e.g., 我不明白你的
话是什么意思。

晁盖来到梁山，梁山的首领王伦拿出酒和菜请晁盖吃饭。

喝酒的时候，晁盖把抢生辰纲的事情说了出来，大家听了都很佩服，纷纷赞美晁盖、吴用他们。王伦却没有说一句① 话②。

晁盖问王伦："您准备怎么安排我们？"

王伦没有回答，只是让晁盖他们先住下，过几天再说。

吴用十分聪明，他马上明白了："王伦嫉妒我们本领比他大，他恐怕不会让我们留在梁山。"

于是吴用就对晁盖说："王伦根本不想让我们留在梁山。我发现林冲对王伦

很不满意，我想一个办法，
让林冲把王伦杀了。"

第二天早上，吴用遇
到林冲，林冲果然对王伦
很不满意，吴用一边劝林
冲不要生气，一边却又用
语言煽动①林冲的怒火②。

又过了一天，王伦把
晁盖、吴用这些人叫到自
己住的地方。他拿出很多
钱，对晁盖说："我很高兴
认识您，可是梁山太小了，
实在留不下你们啊。请大
家收下这些钱，到别的地
方去吧。"

晁盖再三求王伦让大
家留下，王伦却不同意。

林冲十分生气地对王伦
说："你为什么不让晁盖哥
哥和其他兄弟留在梁山？"

① 煽动 (shāndòng) v.
incite
e.g., 他煽动学生，
让学生不来上课。
② 怒火 (nùhuǒ) n.
fury
e.g., 离他远一点儿，
他现在很生气，控
制不了怒火。

王伦对林冲说："你喝醉了吗，敢这么跟我说话？"

林冲说："你什么本领也没有，怎么能当梁山的首领？"

吴用连忙劝林冲："不要生气，都是我们不好，我们马上就走。"

林冲不听吴用的话，他生气地抓住王伦，用刀指着王伦的鼻子说："要你有什么用？"说完，一刀把王伦杀了。

梁山的其他人看见这种情况，吓得都跪在地上。

吴用请林冲当大家的首领。林冲却说："还是让晁盖哥哥当首领吧。"

最后，晁盖当了梁山的首领，吴用排行①第二，

① 排行 (páiháng) v. be ranked as
e.g., 他有两个哥哥和一个弟弟，在家里的排行第三。

公孙胜排行第三，林冲排行第四。

1. 王伦想让晁盖、吴用这七个人留在梁山吗？

2. 谁煽动林冲杀了王伦？

3. 谁当了梁山的新首领？

13．宋江杀死阎婆惜

主要人物和地点：
Main Characters and Places

阎婆惜（Yán Póxī）：宋江的小老婆。
Yan Poxi:　Song Jiang's concubine.

① 封 (fēng) *m.w.* (for sth. enveloped)
e.g., 这儿有你的一封信。

② 信 (xìn) *n.* letter
e.g., 你一定要经常给我写信。

③ 偷偷 (tōutōu) *adv.* secretly
e.g., 趁人不注意，他偷偷地跑了。

宋江在郓城县当一个小官。晁盖感激宋江救过他，就派刘唐去找宋江。

刘唐找到宋江，对他说："晁盖哥哥想念您，让我送来一百两¹黄金，还写了一封①信②给您。"

宋江只拿了信和一根金条²，把其余的黄金还给刘唐，对刘唐说："梁山正是需要钱的时候，你还是把黄金带回去吧。我只要这一根金条，你代替我谢谢晁盖哥哥。"

刘唐送完信就回梁山去了，宋江也回到了家。

宋江的小老婆叫阎婆惜，她又年轻又漂亮。宋江因为工作很忙，经常不回家，于是她偷偷③爱上了别的男人。<u>阎婆惜</u>看见<u>宋江</u>回家，很不高兴。

第二天早上，<u>宋江</u>上班去了。<u>阎婆惜</u>醒了以后，发现床边放着一封信。她读了信，发现那封信竟然是<u>梁山</u>上的强盗<u>晁盖</u>写的。<u>阎婆惜</u>很开心，她准备用这封信威胁①<u>宋江</u>，让<u>宋江</u>把一百两黄金全部交给她。

这时候，<u>宋江</u>发现<u>晁盖</u>的信没有了，赶紧回家找，可是哪儿都没有找到。

<u>宋江</u>想："一定是<u>阎婆惜</u>把信拿走了。"于是他找<u>阎婆惜</u>要。

<u>阎婆惜</u>说："你想把信拿回去，要答应我两件事情。"

① 威胁 (wēixié) *v.*
threaten
e.g., 你不要威胁我，我是不会答应你的。

80

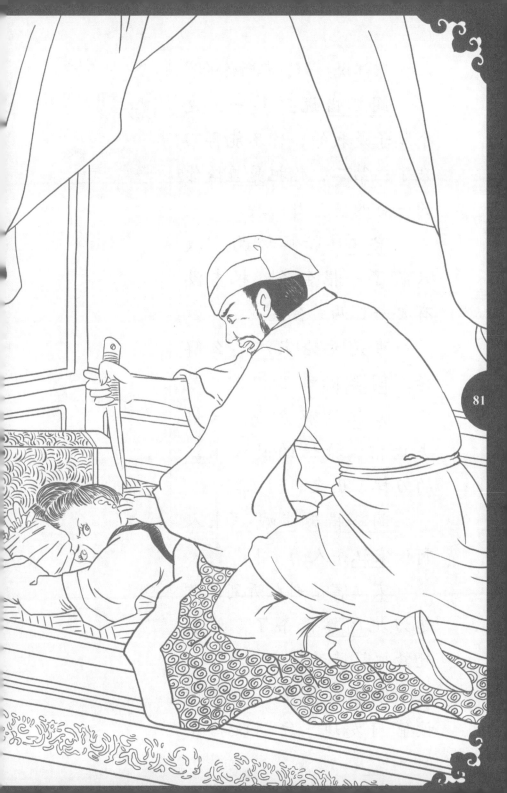

宋江说："好，都听你的。"

阎婆惜说："第一，这个屋子是我的，你不能再回来了；第二，你把晁盖给你的一百两黄金都给我。"

宋江连忙解释说："我只收了一根金条，根本没有要一百两黄金。"

可是无论宋江怎么解释，阎婆惜都不相信。最后，宋江没有办法，只好去抢信。抢信的时候宋江的刀掉了出来。

阎婆惜大声喊："来人啊！宋江杀人啦①！"

宋江害怕别人听到，拿起刀把阎婆惜杀了，然后赶紧把晁盖的信烧②了。

宋江害怕杀人的事情被官府发现，立刻收拾东

① 啦 (lā) *part.* (fusion of 了 and 啊)
e.g., 快走吧，我们已经迟到啦！

② 烧 (shāo) *v.* burn
e.g., 他不小心把衣服烧了一个洞。

82

[1] 两（liǎng）*liang*
两是重量单位，旧时以十六两为一斤（0.5 公斤），现在以十两为一斤。中国古代的货币黄金和白银的都是用"两"计量的。

It is a unit of weight which used to equal 1/16 of a *jin* (500 grams) but now equals 1/10 of a *jin*. Currencies like gold and silver in ancient China were measured by *liang*.

[2] 金条（jīntiáo）gold bar
铸成长条形的黄金，一般每条黄金重十两，也有五两和二十两的金条。

It refers to gold which was cast into a bar shape. Generally, a gold bar weighed ten *liang*, but there were also those which weighed five or twenty *liang* for each.

思考题：

Answer the following questions according to the story.

1. 晁盖是怎么感谢宋江的？

2. 阎婆惜看见宋江回家为什么不高兴？

3. 宋江为什么要杀了阎婆惜？

14．武松景阳冈打老虎

主要人物和地点：
Main Characters and Places

武松（Wǔ Sōng）：本书中的主要人物之一，著名的打虎英雄。他从小习武，武艺高强，性格急侠好义，是一位深受百姓喜爱的英雄。

Wu Song: One of the main characters in the novel. He is also a well-known hero for his killing of the man-eating tiger. He was a great kung fu master who had been studying martial arts since childhood. As a favorite hero among the people, he had a lofty sense of justice and was always ready to help those in need.

景阳冈（Jǐngyáng Gāng）：本书中的一个地名，位于今山东省聊城市。

Jingyang Ridge: A place in the novel located in present-day Liaocheng City, Shandong Province.

① 面 (miàn) *m.w.* (used for flags, mirrors, etc.)
e.g., 桌子上放着一面镜子。

② 旗子 (qízi) *n.* flag, banner
e.g., 教室里挂满了各种颜色的小旗子。

有个叫<u>武松</u>的人，他力气很大，功夫也很厉害。

有一天中午，<u>武松</u>来到<u>景阳冈</u>附近，找了一个酒馆进去吃饭。酒馆的门上挂着一面①旗子②，旗子上写着："三碗不过冈[1]"。

<u>武松</u>坐下，放下手中的武器——木棒。酒馆的老板给<u>武松</u>倒了三碗酒。<u>武松</u>一下就喝光了，说："好酒，再来一碗。"

老板却不再给<u>武松</u>倒酒了。他对<u>武松</u>说："我不能再卖给您酒了，您没有看见旗子上写的'三碗不过冈'吗？"

<u>武松</u>问："什么叫'三碗不过冈'？"

老板说："我们的酒很

厉害，客人喝了三碗就会醉了，根本不能再往景阳冈走。"

武松说："你别胡说，快给我倒酒。"老板只好再给武松倒酒。

武松连续喝了十八碗，大声笑着说："什么'三碗不过冈'，我喝了十八碗都没有醉，哈哈！"给了钱，武松拿着自己的木棒就要走。

看见武松要往景阳冈走，老板着急地说："景阳冈上有一只大老虎，你不要一个人走景阳冈，太危险了。"

武松不相信景阳冈有老虎，无论老板怎么劝，武松就是不听，一个人朝

景阳冈走去。

武松走了一会儿，一只大老虎突然从树林里跳出来，朝武松扑①过去。

武松吓了一跳，迅速躲开，拿起木棒就往老虎身上打。木棒没打中老虎，打在了大树上，断成了两半。老虎又扑了上来，武松一把抓住老虎的头，抬脚使劲往老虎脸上、眼睛上踢。老虎疼得叫了起来，两只脚在地上挖②了个坑③。武松把老虎的头压进坑里，然后又使劲儿往老虎的头上打。最后老虎被武松打死了。

当地的老百姓知道老虎死了，都非常高兴。

从此，武松成为了打

① 扑 (pū) *v.*
spring at
e.g., 孩子高兴地扑到妈妈身上。

② 挖 (wō) *v.* dig
e.g., 我们把这个洞挖开，看看里面有什么。

③ 坑 (kēng) *n.* pit
e.g., 咱们挖一些坑，把小树种进去吧。

老虎的英雄，无论走到哪儿都会受到大家的欢迎，当地的县令还让<u>武松</u>当了一个小官。

[1] 冈（gāng）ridge, low hill
冈是较低平的山岭。但在本文中，"冈"指的就是"景阳冈"。
A low, flat mountain range. In this context, it refers to Jingyang Ridge.

思考题：
Answer the following questions according to the story.

1. 武松喝了三碗酒后，老板为什么不再给武松倒酒了？
2. 武松一共喝了几碗酒？
3. 武松用什么武器打死了老虎？

15. 武松捉弄孙二娘

主要人物和地点：
Main Characters and Places

孙二娘（Sūn Èrniáng）：张青的妻子，与张青在孟州开酒店，
　　后与张青一起加入梁山。
Sun Erniang: Zhang Qing's wife. She ran a pub with her
　　husband in Mengzhou. Later, Sun Erniang and Zhang Qing
　　joined Liangshan.

张青（Zhāng Qīng）：孙二娘的丈夫。
Zhang Qing:　Sun Erniang's husband.

孟州（Mèngzhōu）：中国古代的地名，即今河南省孟州市。
Mengzhou: A place in ancient China situated in present-day
　　Mengzhou City, Henan Province.

① 仇人 (chóurén) *n.* foe
e.g., 他是我们家的仇人。

② 盘 (pán) *m.w.* plate
e.g., 桌子上放着三盘菜。

③ 牛肉 (niúròu) *n.* beef
e.g., 你喜欢吃猪肉还是牛肉?

④ 手 (shǒu) *n.* hand
e.g., 不要碰我的手。

武松刚刚当上小官，就因为杀了害死自己哥哥的仇人①而被发配到孟州。

在去孟州的路上，武松和两个押送他的衙役来到一家酒馆吃饭。三个人坐下，把包裹放在桌子上。

这个时候，一个三十多岁的女人从屋子里走出来，送来了两盘②牛肉③、一大桶酒和几个馒头。趁放馒头的时候，她用手④抓了一下桌子上的包裹，想看看包裹里有多少钱。

武松看见了，想："我听别人说过，这儿有一个酒馆，主人经常用迷药迷倒客人，再抢客人的钱，原来就是这个酒馆啊。看我怎么捉弄你!"

武松对那个女人说："你们这还有更好的酒吗，拿出来让我们尝尝。"

那个女人说："有倒是有，就是容易喝醉。"

武松说："越容易醉越好，赶快拿出来吧。"

那个女人说："您等一下，我马上拿出来。"

那个女人笑着走进屋子，倒了三碗酒，悄悄把一包迷药放进酒里，然后把酒拿出来放到桌子上。两个衙役早就①忍不住，一人喝了一碗酒。武松趁女人不注意，把酒倒在地上，假装喝了这碗酒，大声说："好酒，还是这个酒好。"

两个衙役喝了有迷药的酒，晕了过去，武松也

① 早就 (zǎo jiù) as early as
e.g., 我早就想去泰国旅游了。

92

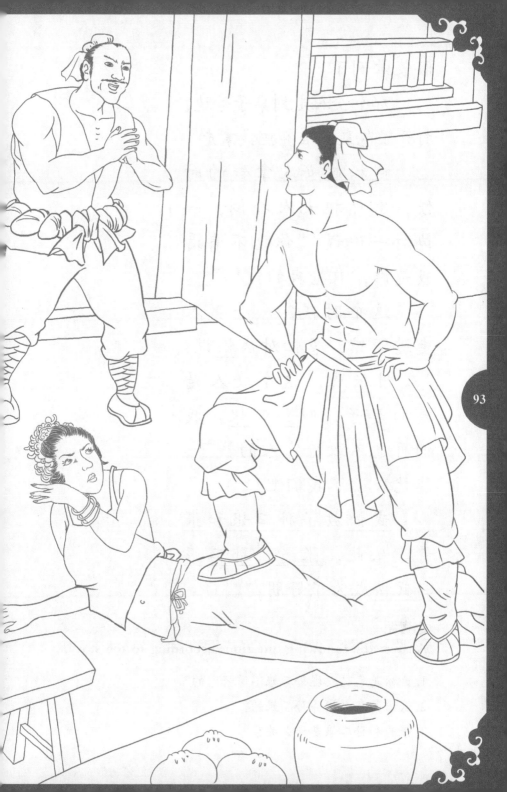

假装晕倒了。

那个女人走到桌子旁边，打开了包裹，准备把钱拿走。

武松趁女人拿钱的时候，突然把女人扑倒，一边打一边说："你也不看看我是谁，敢抢我的钱！"

这个时候，一个男人走进酒馆，急忙对武松说："我叫张青，这个女人是我的妻子，叫孙二娘。我们再也不敢抢客人的钱了，您就饶①了我们吧！"

武松放了孙二娘和张青。从此，张青、孙二娘和武松成为了好朋友。

① 饶 (ráo) *v.* forgive, spare
e.g., 饶了我吧，我再也不敢骗人了。

思考题：
Answer the following questions according to the story.

1. 武松是怎么发现孙二娘不像好人的？
2. 武松是怎么捉弄孙二娘的？
3. 张青和孙二娘是什么关系？

16. 武松醉打蒋门神

主要人物和地点：
Main Characters and Places

蒋门神（Jiǎng Ménshén）：蒋忠的外号。他是张团练的属下，长得又高又壮，有一身好本领，擅长使枪棒，后来被武松杀死。

Door God Jiang: Nickname of Jiang Zhong. As a subordinate of Instructor Zhang, the tall and sturdy Jiang was a skilled fighter and was particularly skillful with spears and sticks. Later, he was killed by Wu Song.

施恩（Shī Ēn）：快活林酒馆的老板，后来加入了梁山。

Shi En: Owner of the Kuaihuolin Inn who joined Liangshan in the end.

武松到了孟州的官府，就被关到监狱里的一个房间。

好几天过去了，监狱领导的儿子施恩每天都派人给武松送吃的和用的东西，但不让人告诉武松是谁送的。武松感到非常奇怪。

一天中午，又有人来送酒和菜，武松不让那个人离开，一定要请送东西的人过来，要不就不吃饭。

那个人无奈，只好去请施恩。

过了一会儿，施恩来到武松的房间，对武松说："我想求您做一件事情，可是又害怕您在路上走得太累，没有力气，所以想让

① 外号 (wàihào) *n.*
nickname
e.g., 他外号白马王
子。

您休息几天。"

武松说："去年我生病的时候，景阳冈上的老虎都被我打死了。你就说什么事情吧！"

施恩把自己的事情告诉了武松。

原来，施恩开了一个酒馆。最近有一个外号① 叫蒋门神的人抢走了施恩的酒馆，还把施恩打了。施恩求武松帮助他抢回酒馆。

武松大笑着说："我最讨厌抢别人东西的人，走，咱们去找这个人。"

武松找到了蒋门神。蒋门神知道武松是施恩请来的人，就朝武松扑过来，想把武松打死。

武松一脚就踢倒了蒋

门神，然后把蒋门神按在地上打，打得蒋门神大喊："不要杀我！"

武松踩着蒋门神说："你只要答应我三件事情，我就放了你。"

蒋门神说："别说三件，就是三百件事情我都答应。"

武松说："第一，你立刻把这个酒馆还给施恩；第二，你要给施恩道歉；第三，你马上离开孟州，要不我以后看见你一次就打你一次。"

蒋门神说："行，我都答应您。"

武松听到蒋门神答应了这三件事情，就把蒋门神放了。他对蒋门神说：

"我连老虎都打死过，别说是你了。"

蒋门神这才知道原来打自己的人是武松。

从此，施恩又成了酒馆的主人。可是蒋门神却非常恨武松，一直想报仇①。

① 报仇 (bàochóu) v. take revenge
e.g., 他的父亲被别人打了，他想为他父亲报仇。

100

思考题：
Answer the following questions according to the story.

1. 施恩为什么每天给武松送吃的和用的东西？

2. 武松要蒋门神答应他哪三件事？

3. 武松帮施恩夺回快活林的酒馆了吗？

17. 张都监陷害武松

主要人物和地点：
Main Characters and Places

张都监（Zhāng dūjiān）：孟州管理兵马的大官，后来被武松杀死。

Inspector Zhang: A high-ranking official who was in charge of the military forces in Mengzhou. He was later killed by Wu Song.

张团练（Zhāng tuánliàn）：张都监的结义兄弟，后被武松杀死。

Instructor Zhang: He and Inspector Zhang are sworn brothers who were both killed by Wu Song in the end.

恩州（Ēnzhōu）：中国古代的地名，在今河北省清河县。恩州在北宋时是辽与北宋的边境地区，经常打仗，贫穷落后，是北宋官府流放犯人的地方。

Enzhou: A place in ancient China located in present-day Qinghe County, Hebei Province. During the Northern Song Dynasty, Enzhou was located in the border area between Liao (a state located to the north of Song) and Song. This area suffered many wars and utter poverty. Many convicts were exiled to Enzhou by the Northern Song government.

武松打了蒋门神，蒋门神非常恨武松，一直在找机会陷害①他。

有一天，孟州的大官张都监对武松说："我想请您在我家保护我。"

武松觉得这个工作很好，就答应了。从此，他就跟着张都监。张都监对武松很好，还要把家里的丫鬟嫁给武松，武松很感动。

有一天晚上，武松忽然听到有人喊："抓小偷啊！"

武松赶紧冲了过去，问："小偷在哪儿？"

那个要嫁给武松的丫鬟说："小偷逃到花园②里了。"

① 陷害 (xiànhài) v.
frame up
e.g., 我不是小偷，是他们陷害我的。

② 花园 (huāyuán) n.
garden
e.g., 你的房间后面就是一个漂亮的花园啊。

① 箱子 (xiāngzi) n.
trunk
e.g., 你把现在不穿
的衣服都放进这个
箱子里。

② 偷 (tōu) v. steal
e.g., 他就是小偷，
刚才在公共汽车上
偷了我的钱。

武松又赶紧赶到花园。正在这个时候，七八个士兵冲进花园，把他捆了起来。然后他们派人来搜武松的房间，发现武松床下有个箱子①，箱子里的宝贝都是张都监家里的。武松不知道怎么解释，只好一句话不说。

第二天，张都监让士兵把武松送到官府。施恩知道武松被抓，赶紧带着钱找到管理监狱的小官。

小官对施恩说："这一切都是张都监和张团练两个人的主意，他们故意陷害武松偷②东西。蒋门神就躲在张团练的家里。"

为了救武松，施恩到处求人帮忙，还给了知府

① 暗号 (ànhào) n.
secret signal
e.g., 我看不懂你给
我的暗号。

② 河 (hé) n. river
e.g., 这条大河就是
黄河吧?

很多钱。所以武松没有被判杀头,而是被发配到恩州。

两个衙役负责押送武松。半路上,施恩找到武松,悄悄告诉他:"那两个衙役,我看不像好人,你路上千万要小心啊!"说完,施恩就离开了。

武松和两个衙役继续往恩州走去。路上遇到两个人,都拿着刀,于是五个人一起上路。这四个人偷偷打暗号①要杀死武松,被武松看了出来。

他们来到一条大河②旁边,河上有一座桥。武松忽然转过身,两脚把两个衙役踢到了河里。另外两个人赶快往桥下跑,武松追上去，先杀了其中一个人，然后抓着另①一个，问是谁派他们来的。

那个人说："我们俩是蒋门神派来的，张团练和蒋门神命令我们在路上杀了你。"

武松问："蒋门神在哪里？"

那个人说："蒋门神和张团练现在都在张都监家的鸳鸯楼上喝酒。"

武松听完，生气地把这个人也杀了，然后去鸳鸯楼报仇。

① 另 (lìng) *pron.* other
e.g., 这道题还有另一个答案。

思考题：

Answer the following questions according to the story.

1. 张都监为什么请武松保护自己？

2. 张都监和蒋门神是怎么陷害武松的？

3. 在武松去恩州的路上，施恩提醒武松小心什么？

18. 武松鸳鸯楼报仇

主要人物和地点：
Main Characters and Places

鸳鸯楼（Yuānyang Lóu）：张都监家中请客的地方。
Lovebirds Tower: It's located within Inspector Zhang's residence. He often treated guests here.

武松杀了四个来杀他的人，然后回到孟州找张都监、张团练和蒋门神报仇。

这个时候，张都监、张团练和蒋门神正在鸳鸯楼的房间里喝酒。武松悄悄上楼，在门外听到蒋门神说："谢谢大人帮助我们杀了武松。"

又听张都监说："如果不是张团练请我帮助你，我才不想管①这件事情呢。"说完，三个人开始喝酒，庆祝杀了武松。

武松听到这些话，生气地踢开房间的门。三个人看见武松，吓得手里拿的杯子都掉了。蒋门神还没有来得及动②一下，就被武松的刀砍倒在地上。

① 管 (guǎn) v. attend to, interfere e.g., 这件事我们不能不管。

② 动 (dòng) v. move e.g., 你站着别动，我要给你照相。

打虎武松

救人者

109

张都监刚想逃，武松拿着刀朝张都监的头砍去，一刀就把张都监的脑袋砍掉了。

张团练把椅子举起来，使劲儿朝武松扔来，武松接住椅子，又朝张团练扔去，张团练被椅子砸①倒了。武松走过去，拿刀砍死了张团练。

武松对着地上的三个死人说："我是打死老虎的英雄，却被你们这些人陷害，今天我杀了你们，真是太对了。"

武松又想起来，万一别人为了这件事情被抓，就不好了。于是，他用死人的血在墙上写了几个字："杀人者打虎武松也"（就

① 砸 (zá) v.
pound, hit
e.g., 石头砸到我的脚了。

① 天 (tiān) *n.* sky
e.g., 天还没有黑，
我们再玩一会儿吧。

是"杀人的是打虎的<u>武松</u>"的意思）。

　　<u>武松</u>拿着刀，趁天 ① 黑逃出了<u>孟州</u>。

思考题：
Answer the following questions according to the story.

1. <u>武松</u>为什么又回到<u>孟州</u>？

2. 陷害<u>武松</u>的是哪几个人？

3. <u>武松</u>为什么杀了人后，在墙上写"杀人者打虎武松也"？

19. 花荣大闹清风寨

主要人物和地点：
Main Characters and Places

花荣（Huā Róng）：清风寨的首领，有"百步穿杨"的功夫，
人称"小李广"，后来加入梁山。

Hua Rong: A chief of the Qingfeng Stronghold who was known for
shooting arrows with great precision. He joined Liangshan afterwards.

刘高（Liú Gāo）：清风寨的另一个首领。他没有什么本事，
当上首领后为非作歹，和花荣关系不好。

Liu Gao: The other chief of Qingfeng Stronghold. He was a
man without any remarkable skills and quickly turned evil
after becoming the head of the stronghold. He did not get
along well with Hua Rong.

清风寨（Qīngfēng Zhài）：一处具有军事防御功能的城堡，位
于今山东省青州市。

Qingfeng Stronghold: A stronghold located in present-day Qingzhou
City, Shandong Province.

清风山（Qīngfēng Shān）：位于今河南省义马市，山上有一伙
强盗。

Qingfeng Mountain: A mountain located in present-day Yima City,
Henan Province. A group of bandits resided there.

① 射 (shè) *v.* shoot
e.g., 他朝敌人射了
三支箭。

② 箭 (jiàn) *n.* arrow
e.g., 箭在古代是很
著名的武器。

③ 面子 (miànzi) *n.*
face, reputation
e.g., 他在朋友聚会
的时候骂我，我觉
得很没有面子。

宋江杀了阎婆惜，离开郓城县，去找以前的朋友花荣。花荣是清风寨的首领。他射①箭②的本领很厉害。

宋江在去清风寨的路上，路过清风山。清风山上有一群强盗，他们很佩服宋江，一定要宋江在清风山住几天，宋江答应了。

一天，这群强盗从山下抢来一个女人，这个女人是清风寨另一个首领刘高的妻子。

宋江就对清风山的强盗说："我正要去清风寨，看在我的面子③上，把这个女人放了吧。"

那些强盗很尊敬宋江，就把这个女人放了。

过了几天，宋江来到清风寨，花荣让人带着宋江逛逛清风寨。

宋江正走着，遇到了刘高和妻子。刘高的妻子看见了宋江，马上指着宋江跟刘高说："那个人是清风山的强盗。"

刘高派了一群人去抓宋江，准备第二天把宋江送到官府。

花荣的人看见宋江被抓，马上赶回去向花荣报告。花荣急忙带着几十个士兵来到刘高的家，救出了宋江。

刘高十分生气，他让两个很有本领的人带着几百个人来到花荣的家，想再把宋江抢走。

花荣对刘高的人说：
"这是我和刘高的事情，
跟你们没有关系，今天让
你们看看我射箭的本领。
看我先射左边门神的武
器。"说完，花荣就射出
一支箭，正好射中 ^① 左边
门神的武器。

花荣又说："看我射右
边门神的帽子。"说完，花
荣又射出一支箭，也射中
了右边门神的帽子。

花荣接着说："看你们
中间那个穿白色衣服的人，
我要射他的心脏。"穿白色
衣服的人一听到这句话，
马上逃走了，其他士兵也
跟着他跑了。

花荣害怕刘高再派人

① 中 (zhòng) v. hit
e.g., 他猜中了这个
题目的答案。

116

来抢宋江，就和宋江一起
离开清风寨，来到了清风山。

117

思考题：
Answer the following questions according to the story.

1. 宋江救了刘高的妻子，刘高为什么还要抓宋江？
2. 刘高和花荣是什么关系？
3. 花荣射箭的本领怎么样？

20. 宋江喝醉写反诗

主要人物和地点：
Main Characters and Places

黄文炳（Huáng Wénbǐng）：向知府告密宋江写"反诗"的人，后来被梁山好汉杀死。

Huang Wenbing: He noticed the poem written by Song Jiang and informed the prefect. In the end, he was killed by the outlaws from Liangshan.

江州（Jiāngzhōu）：中国古代的地名，位于今江西省九江市。

Jiangzhou: A place in ancient China located in present-day Jiujiang City, Jiangxi Province.

浔阳楼（Xúnyáng Lóu）：位于今江西省九江市，因九江古称浔阳而得名浔阳楼。本书中的浔阳楼是一家著名的酒馆。

Xunyanglou: A famous restaurant located in present-day Jiujiang City, Jiangxi Province. Jiujiang was called Xunyang in ancient times, hence the name of the restaurant.

山东（Shāndōng）：北宋时期的省级地方行政区划，大体与今山东省一致。梁山即位于山东境内。

Shandong: A provincial administrative region during the Northern Song Dynasty, approximately the same as present-day Shandong Province. Liangshan was located in Shandong.

① 笔 (bǐ) *n.* brush,
pen
e.g., 我的笔坏了，
能借给我一支笔吗？

宋江和花荣在清风山住了一段时间，花荣劝宋江一起去梁山做强盗，宋江一直没有答应。

这个时候，宋江的父亲让宋江的弟弟给宋江写信，说自己死了，骗宋江回家。宋江回家后，宋江的父亲劝他向官府自首，宋江就去自首了，官府把宋江发配到了江州。

宋江来到江州后的一天，他走进江州著名的浔阳楼，找到一个座位坐下，开始喝酒。

宋江喝了很多酒，已经有些醉了。他让酒馆的人拿来笔①，一边喝酒一边在墙上写了一首诗："心在山东身在吴[1]，飘蓬江海漫嗟吁[2]。他时若遂凌云志[3]，敢笑黄巢不丈夫。[4]"写完诗，他又在墙上写了五个字：郓城宋江作。

接着，宋江又喝了一会儿酒，就离开浔阳楼，回家睡觉了。第二天早上起床，他已经完全忘记了这件事情。

江州有一个叫黄文炳的人，他来到浔阳楼，在墙上发现了宋江写的诗。黄文炳十分吃惊，他认为这是一首反诗[5]，就向知府报告了这件事情，并且拿出抄下来的诗给知府看。

知府说："几天以前，我父亲给我写了一封信，信上说，东京现在流行着四句话，'耗国因家木，刀

心在山东身在吴

飘蓬江海谩嗟吁

他时若遂凌云志

敢笑黄巢不丈夫

郓城宋江

兵点水工。纵横三十六，播乱在山东。'6'他让我在江州注意一下。"

黄文炳想了一会儿，对知府说："'耗国因家木'，这是说浪费国家财产的人，一定是'家'字的'宀'下加一个'木'字，就是'宋'这个字。'刀兵点水工'，这是说掌握士兵的人，是'水'字加一个'工'字，这不是'江'字吗？这说明谋反①的人是宋江，而宋江写的诗也表达了他想谋反的意思。"

知府马上派人去抓宋江。有人已经提前把消息告诉了宋江，可是宋江还是没有成功逃走，被知府关进了监狱。

① 谋反 (móufǎn) v. conspire against the state
e.g., 在中国古代，谋反指试图推翻政府的行为。

122

[1] 心在山东身在吴（xīn zài Shāndōng shēn zài Wú）宋江的家在山东郓城县，他被发配至江州，江州属于吴地。这句话的意思是"我虽然待在江州，但我的心却还在家乡山东省郓城县。"

This sentence shows Song Jiang's hometown was Yuncheng County in Shandong Province, but he was exiled to Jiangzhou which belonged to the Wu region.

[2] 飘蓬江海漫嗟吁（piāopéng jiānghǎi màn jiēxū）"飘蓬"比喻漂泊不定，"嗟吁"是叹息的意思。这句话的意思是"总是感叹我漂泊不定的生活"。
飘蓬 means to wander around and 嗟吁 means to sigh. This sentence referenced Song Jiang's inability to settle down and live a stable life.

[3] 他时若遂凌云志（tāshí ruò suì língyún zhì）"凌云志"指远大的志向。这句话的意思是"希望有一天，我可以实现远大的志向"。
凌云志 means lofty and noble ambitions. This sentence expressed Song Jiang's lofty aspiration.

[4] 敢笑黄巢不丈夫（gǎn xiào Huáng Cháo bú zhàngfu）"敢"是谁也不敢的意思，"黄巢"是唐朝末年反政府的农民起义军领袖。这句话的意思是"谁也不敢嘲笑黄巢不是英雄"。黄巢是农民起义军的领袖，也是谋反的象征。这首诗因为提到黄巢，并且宋江表现出十分钦佩黄巢，所以黄文炳和知府认为这首诗是反诗，宋江想谋反。
敢 implies that people dare not. 黄巢, Huang Chao, was the leader of the rebellious peasants who fought against the government during the last years of the Tang Dynasty (618-907). The name of Huang Chao thus became the representation of rebellion. Song Jiang admired Huang Chao for his principles, so in this part of the story, Huang Wenbing and the prefect thought the poem revealed rebellious motives and thus regarded Song Jiang as a rebel.

[5] 反诗（fǎnshī）poem with rebellious motives
反诗指具有反政府含义的诗。在中国古代，当社会极度黑暗时，常会有这类诗出现，目的是破坏政府的威信。
The term refers to poems with rebellious motives against the government. In ancient China, this kind of poetry often appeared when the government became overtly and widely corrupted. The purpose of this kind of poetry was to undermine the credibility of the government.

[6] 耗国因家木，刀兵点水工。纵横三十六，播乱在山东。（Hào guó yīn jiā mù, dāobīng diǎn shuǐ gōng. Zònghéng sānshíliù, bōluàn zài Shāndōng.）这四句话的意思是"想谋反的人姓宋名江，他聚集了三十六个英雄好汉，谋反的地方在山东"。这四句话验证了宋江写的诗是反诗。
The four sentences alluded to the fact that the rebel was named Song Jiang. He was supported by 36 outlaws with whom he started a rebellion in Shandong. The four sentences seemed to verify that Song Jiang wanted to rebel against the government.

1. 宋江为什么离开花荣回了家？

2. 黄文炳是怎么看宋江写的诗的？

3. 宋江为什么被关进了监狱？

21. 梁山英雄救宋江

主要人物和地点：
Main Characters and Places

戴宗（Dài Zōng）：江州知府的下属，喜欢交朋友，讲义气，做事情稍有心机，和宋江一起加入梁山。

Dai Zong: A subordinate of the Jiangzhou prefect. He liked making friends and was sophisticated but very loyal to his friends. He joined Liangshan with Song Jiang.

李逵（Lǐ Kuí）：本书中的重要人物之一，长得又黑又壮，武艺高强，习惯用斧子做武器，绰号"黑旋风"，后跟着宋江加入梁山。

Li Kui: An important character in the novel. He was a muscular man with a dark complexion. Adept at martial arts, his favorite weapons were two axes. He was nicknamed the Black Whirlwind. Later, Li Kui followed Song Jiang and joined Liangshan.

宋江被江州知府关进了监狱。知府派戴宗去东京，询问蔡京应该怎么处理这件事情。

戴宗是宋江的好朋友，他没有直接去东京，而是先来到梁山，跟大家商量怎么救宋江。

吴用想在宋江去东京的路上救宋江。于是他模仿蔡京的字写了一封信，信里的意思是：命令江州知府把宋江送到东京。

戴宗把这封信交给了知府。信里的字模仿得很像，知府没有看出它是假的。但是，狡猾的黄文炳却发现信上的印章①是假的，并且告诉了知府。知府非常生气，他把戴宗也关进了监狱，准

① 印章 (yìnzhāng) *n.* seal
e.g., 这份文件要签字并且盖印章。

① 里面 (lǐmiàn) *n.*
inside
e.g., 教室里面坐满
了学生。

② 强壮 (qiángzhuàng)
adj. strong, sturdy
e.g., 他十分强壮，
一看就没有生病。

备把宋江和戴宗一起杀了。

梁山的人收到了这个消息，打算去江州，救出宋江和戴宗。

到了杀宋江和戴宗的那一天，知府派了很多人，把宋江和戴宗押送到刑场¹，要在中午杀了他们。

江州的老百姓都来到了刑场，一些拿着蛇和拿着刀的人也走进刑场里面①。士兵想把老百姓赶走，可是老百姓不愿意走。

到了中午，知府命令刽子手²杀了宋江和戴宗。

突然，拿蛇的人把蛇扔在地上，大家害怕极了，刑场变得很乱。这时候，一个又黑又强壮②的男人突然跳出来，这个人就是李

① 斧子 (fǔzi) *n.* ax
e.g., 他用斧子砍树。

達。他举起斧子 ①，把刽子手砍死了。

拿刀的人来到宋江和戴宗的旁边，背着两个人就跑，其余的人负责保护他们逃出刑场。

原来拿蛇和拿刀的人都是梁山的首领晁盖派来的。梁山的人救了宋江和戴宗，从此这两个人就留在了梁山。

[1] 刑场（xíngchǎng）execution ground
刑场指对犯人执行死刑的场所。
The term refers to the place where the criminals are executed.

[2] 刽子手（guìzishǒu）headsman
在中国古代，刽子手指以处决犯人为职业的人。刽子手一般用刀砍断犯人的头。
In ancient China, headsmen were people who executed criminals. In most cases, the executioner would behead the prisoner.

思考题：
Answer the following questions according to the story.

1. 宋江和戴宗是什么关系？
2. 江州知府怎么发现蔡京的信是假的？
3. 最后，梁山的人用什么方法在刑场里救了宋江和戴宗？

22. 真李逵与假李逵

主要人物和地点：
Main Characters and Places

李鬼（Lǐ Guǐ）：假冒李逵拦路抢劫的人。

Li Gui: A man who impersonated Li Kui and robbed passers-by in the woods.

① 冒充 (màochōng)
v. impersonate,
pass ... off as
e.g., 我们拒绝使用
不合格的产品冒充
合格的产品。

李逵很想念家里的母亲。他准备回家，把母亲接到梁山，跟他一起生活。

在回家的路上，李逵经过一片树林。

突然，一个男人从树林里跳出来，他拿着斧子，对着李逵大声喊："知道我是谁吗？我就是李逵！怎么样，害怕了吧？只要你把所有的钱都给我，我就不杀你。"

李逵听了，大笑起来："我就是李逵。你看看你的丑样子，竟然敢冒充①我，还敢抢钱！"说完，李逵拿着刀朝他砍去。

假李逵吓得急忙说："您饶了我吧。我叫李鬼，就住在附近。我家里还有一位八十多岁的母亲，我

131

① 赡养 (shànyǎng) v.
provide for
e.g., 我们要孝顺父亲
和母亲，努力赡养他
们。

在树林里抢钱，是为了要赡养①母亲。您很有名，每个人都害怕您，所以我才冒充您的名字。"

李逵被李鬼的话感动了，他想："原来李鬼和我一样，也有一个母亲要赡养。他是一个孝顺的人，我不能杀他。"

李逵放了李鬼，又给了李鬼一些钱，让李鬼去做生意，赚钱赡养母亲。

李鬼拿了钱，感激地说："谢谢您不杀我。我保证以后不再冒充您，也不抢别人的钱了。"说完，李鬼离开了这片树林。

李逵继续往家走，又累又饿地来到一个房子外面。房子里有一个女人，李逵让那个女人卖给他一些吃的东西。

　　那个女人不敢拒绝，只好走进厨房给李逵找吃的东西。

　　这个时候，李逵听到厨房里面有一个人对这个女人说："我今天太倒霉了，居然遇到了真的李逵。幸亏我聪明，骗他说我有一个母亲，要不我肯定会被他杀死的。他特别傻，马上就相信了我的话，不仅放了我，还给了我很多钱。"原来这个房子就是李鬼的家，那个女人是李鬼的老婆。

　　李鬼的老婆赶紧说："你小声一点儿。刚才来了一个又黑又强壮的男人，就在房间外面呢。你去看看是不是李逵。"

李鬼说:"如果是他,我们就在米饭里放一点儿迷药,把他弄晕,然后杀了他。抢了他的钱,咱们就可以搬到城市里住了。"

李逵听了这些话,非常生气:"我给了他钱,又放了他,他竟然想杀我!"他冲进厨房里,一刀杀死了李鬼。

李鬼的老婆趁李逵不注意,悄悄地逃走了。

李逵在厨房找了一些吃的东西,然后烧了这个房子,继续往家乡走去。

思考题:

Answer the following questions according to the story.

1. 李鬼为什么要冒充李逵?

2. 李鬼说,他的家里有一位八十多岁的母亲,这是真的吗,为什么?

3. 最后,李鬼和妻子准备对李逵做什么?

23. 李逵杀老虎

主要人物和地点：
Main Characters and Places

李达（Lǐ Dá）：李逵的哥哥。
Li Da: Li Kui's elder brother.

李逵回到自己家里，发现母亲的眼睛瞎了。他伤心地说："妈妈，我是李逵啊，我回来了。"

李逵的母亲躺在床上高兴地说："儿子，你终于回来了。我经常想念你，哭得连眼睛都瞎了。"

李逵很难受，他骗母亲说："我现在做了官，这次我回家，是想接您去我住的地方。"

李逵的母亲高兴地说："太好了，等你哥哥回来，我们一起去。"

这个时候，李逵的哥哥李达回来了。李达看见李逵，先是十分吃惊，接着生气地说："我还以为你永远不会回来呢！"

李逵的妈妈赶紧说："李逵做了官，要接我们一起走呢。"

李达说："妈妈，他骗你呢，你别相信他说的话。他杀了人，官府正在抓他呢。"李达说完就离开了家。

李逵想："哥哥出去，可能是去找人抓我，我还是赶紧走吧。"

他给哥哥留下一些钱，就背着母亲离开了家，往梁山走去。

这天晚上，李逵背着母亲来到一座大山。他让母亲坐在一块石头上，自己去找喝的水。等李逵回来的时候，却发现母亲不见了，地上有血。

李逵十分慌张，他

① 沿 (yán) prep.
along
e.g., 你沿着这条路走下去，就能见到博物馆。

② 山洞 (shāndòng) n.
mountain cave
e.g., 我们在爬山的时候，发现了一个山洞。

③ 愤怒 (fènnù) adj.
angry, furious
e.g., 他用愤怒的眼神看着我。

沿①着血走，来到一个山洞②，看见洞里有两只小老虎，正在吃一条人腿。

李逵心想："原来我的母亲被老虎吃了！"李逵发现这条腿是他母亲的腿，非常生气和难过，他拿着刀上前，把两只小老虎都杀了。

正在这个时候，两只大老虎走到洞口，它们看见李逵杀了自己的孩子，愤怒③地扑向李逵。李逵一点儿也不害怕，他拿着刀朝一只老虎的脖子砍去，把这只老虎的脑袋砍断了，接着又拿刀砍向另一只老虎的肚子。老虎痛苦地大叫一声，从洞口逃了出去，一会儿就倒在地上死了。

140

① 埋 (mái) *v.* bury
e.g., 路已经被大雪埋住了。

② 尸体 (shītǐ) *n.* dead body
e.g., 人和动物死后的身体就是尸体。

　　李逵杀了四只老虎，哭着埋①了母亲的尸体②，又跪在地上哭了很长时间，才离开这里。

思考题：
Answer the following questions according to the story.

1. 李逵母亲的眼睛为什么瞎了？

2. 李逵找水回来，为什么没有在树林里找到妈妈？

3. 李逵一共杀了几只老虎？

24. 朱贵兄弟救李逵

主要人物和地点：
Main Characters and Places

曹太公（Cáo tàigōng）：一个小镇的大地主。
Squire Cao: A rich landlord of a small town.

朱富（Zhū Fù）：朱贵的弟弟，擅长使用暗器，在梁山负责监造、供应酒、醋。
Zhu Fu: Zhu Gui's younger brother. He was adept at using hidden weapons. At Liangshan, he was in charge of brewing and supplying liquor and vinegar.

李云（Lǐ Yún）：朱富的师父，武艺高强，原来是沂水县的小官，后不得已加入梁山。
Li Yun: The master of Zhu Fu. He excelled in martial arts. He used to be a junior official in Yishui County. In the end, Li Yun went to Liangshan for shelter.

① 地主 (dìzhǔ) n.
landlord
e.g., 地主家里有很
多土地。

李逵埋了母亲的尸体，离开了那座山，来到一个小镇[1]。

李逵在小镇上遇到了李鬼的老婆。李鬼的老婆看见李逵，赶紧向大地主① 曹太公报告。曹太公听了李鬼老婆的话，高兴得不得了，他想："抓住了李逵，官府一定会给我很多钱的。"

可是李逵的功夫很厉害，怎么抓他呢？曹太公想出了一个办法。他准备了很多酒和菜，把李逵请到家里喝酒。李逵很高兴地跟曹太公一边喝酒，一边聊天，一会儿就喝醉了。

曹太公让人把李逵捆起来，又派李鬼的老婆去官府报告。

官府马上派人来小镇，把李逵押送回官府。

李逵离开梁山的时候，宋江害怕李逵闯祸①，派朱贵悄悄保护他。朱贵听到李逵被抓了，很着急，但不知道应该怎么办。

朱贵的弟弟朱富想了想，说："我有办法可以救李逵。押送李逵的李云是我的师父²，我可以假装祝贺他抓到李逵，然后用迷药弄晕他。"朱贵同意了。

于是，朱贵兄弟带着放了迷药的酒和菜，在李云经过的路上等着。

过了一会儿，朱贵看见一大群人走来。李云走在前面押送着李逵，曹太

① 闯祸 (chuǎnghuò)
v. cause troubles
e.g., 他们不喜欢这个总是闯祸的孩子。

公和李鬼的老婆也在这群人里，他们俩正高兴呢，觉得自己抓了李逵，官府一定会给自己很多钱。

朱富拿了一碗酒，对李云说："师父，我祝贺你抓到李逵！"

李云十分高兴，他和押送李逵的人把酒和菜都吃完了。过了一会儿，大家纷纷倒在地上。

李云大叫一声："不好，上当了。"他刚想逃走，却觉得头很晕，也摔倒在地上。

朱贵和朱富弄断了捆李逵的绳子，李逵从地上拿起一把刀，杀死了李鬼的老婆和曹太公。

朱富劝李云跟自己一起去梁山，李云害怕官府

① 追究 (zhuījiū) *v.*
investigate,
look into
e.g., 这件事情造成
了严重的后果，我
们一定要追究主要
责任。

追究 ① 自己的责任，只好
同意了。四个人一起上了
<u>梁山</u>。

[1] 镇（zhèn）town, township
镇是行政区划单位，一般由县一级领导。
It is an administrative unit under the county level.

[2] 师父（shīfu）master, mentor
武术、戏剧等传统技艺领域中传授技艺的老师。
A mentor who teaches traditional techniques such as martial arts and drama.

思考题：
Answer the following questions according to the story.

1. 曹太公是怎么抓住李逵的？

2. 朱贵和朱富使用了什么办法救李逵？

3. 李鬼的老婆和曹太公最后怎么样了？

25. 宋江攻打祝家庄

主要人物和地点：
Main Characters and Places

祝朝奉（Zhù Cháofèng）：梁山附近的祝家庄的主人，有三个儿子。祝朝奉依仗着官府的势力，为非作歹，专门与梁山作对。

Zhu Chaofeng: The headman of Zhu's Family Town which was located nearby Liangshan and the father of three sons. He had connections with the local government and abused his authority and wealth by oppressing the people. He considered the people of Liangshan to be his enemies and provoked them many times.

石秀（Shí Xiù）：金陵（今南京）人，自幼父母双亡，流落河北蓟州，只能靠卖柴生活，有一身好武艺，爱打抱不平。

Shi Xiu: A native of Jinling (present-day Nanjing), who became an orphan at a very young age. He wandered to Jizhou, Hebei Province and made a living by selling firewood. He was well-trained in martial arts and always helped those who were oppressed or in need.

祝家庄（Zhùjiā Zhuāng）：位于梁山附近的一个小镇，主人是祝朝奉。

Zhu's Family Town: A small town near Liangshan. The headman of the town was Zhu Chaofeng.

① 消灭 (xiāomiè) v.
wipe out
e.g., 我们要消灭敌人。

② 攻打 (gōngdǎ) v.
attack, assault
e.g., 敌人正派士兵攻打我们的首都。

③ 探路 (tànlù) v.
explore the way
e.g., 你先去前面探路，我们马上就来。

梁山附近有一个祝家庄，主人是祝朝奉。祝家庄与梁山的关系不好，祝家庄把梁山当成敌人，一直想消灭①梁山。梁山的时任被祝家庄抓住后，宋江打算攻打②祝家庄，消灭祝家庄。可是祝家庄的路非常难走，不熟悉的人很容易迷路。因此，宋江带着人在祝家庄外等着，先派石秀去祝家庄探路③。

石秀进了祝家庄，一个老人对他说："你不是祝家庄的人吧？赶快离开吧，祝家庄要有危险了。"

石秀假装吃惊地问："怎么会有危险呢？"

老人解释说："祝家庄和梁山的关系不好，宋江准备要攻打我们了。"

石秀假装害怕地哭了起来："我不想死在祝家庄啊！您给我指一条能走出去的路吧，我想回家。"

老人觉得石秀可怜，就告诉他："你只要看见白杨树①就拐弯，千万要记得，没有白杨树的路是走不出祝家庄的。"

石秀对老人说了声谢谢，刚要离开，就听到有人喊："大家都注意啦！今天晚上梁山的人要来，我们把红灯作为信号，只要看见红灯，大家就一起冲过去抓人。"

石秀一直没有走出祝家庄，宋江非常着急。他带着人冲进祝家庄，想救

① 白杨树 (báiyángshù)
n. white poplar
e.g., 白杨树主要分布在中国北方。

石秀。可是，走了一会儿大家就迷路了。就在宋江不知道往哪儿走的时候，祝家庄的人开始朝宋江他们射箭，很多士兵都被箭射死了。宋江无奈地说："没有想到，我们就要死在祝家庄了。"

这个时候，突然有人喊："只要看见白杨树就拐弯，我们一定能走出去。"原来，石秀赶来救大家了。

走了一会儿，周围的祝家庄士兵越来越多。石秀说："他们把红灯作为信号，我们往哪走，那个人就举着红灯往哪走，所以祝家庄的士兵就都朝我们来了。"

花荣说："我有办法。"

152

说完，他射出一支箭，把红灯射灭了。

红灯没有了，<u>祝家庄</u>的人就不知道应该往哪儿走了。<u>宋江</u>赶紧带着大家冲出<u>祝家庄</u>，回到了<u>梁山</u>。

思考题：

Answer the following questions according to the story.

1. 宋江为什么先派石秀进入祝家庄？
2. 祝家庄的红灯是用来做什么的？
3. 谁射灭了祝家庄的红灯？

26. 顾大嫂监狱救兄弟

主要人物和地点：
Main Characters and Places

孙新（Sūn Xīn）：海南人，随哥哥孙立来到登州，娶了顾大嫂为妻，后加入梁山。

Sun Xin: A native of Hainan who came to Dengzhou with his elder brother Sun Li. He later married Sister Gu and joined Liangshan in the end.

顾大嫂（Gù dàsǎo）：孙新的妻子，梁山第二位女将，有一身本领，后随丈夫孙新一起加入梁山。

Sister Gu: Wife of Sun Xin. She had good fighting skills and was the second female to become an outlaw leader at Liangshan. She joined the outlaws with her husband Sun Xin.

解珍（Xiè Zhēn）：解宝的哥哥，山东登州人。兄弟俩后随孙新等人加入梁山。

Xie Zhen: A native of Dengzhou of Shandong. He is the elder brother of Xie Bao. The Xie brothers joined Liangshan with Sun Xin and the others.

解宝（Xiè Bǎo）：猎人，解珍的弟弟，山东登州人。

Xie Bao: A hunter in Dengzhou, Shandong Province. Xie Zhen's younger brother.

毛太公（Máo tàigōng）：山东登州一个有权有势的人。

Squire Mao: A powerful man who lived in Dengzhou, Shandong Province.

孙立（Sūn Lì）：孙新的哥哥，在登州是管理士兵的官员，后跟着孙新加入了梁山。

Sun Li: Sun Xin's elder brother. He was the officer in charge of management of soldiers at Dengzhou. Later, he joined Liangshan with Sun Xin.

登州（Dēngzhōu）：中国古代的地名，位于今山东省烟台市
　　附近。

Dengzhou: A place in ancient China located near present-day
　　Yantai City, Shandong Province.

155

登州有一个酒馆，酒馆的老板叫孙新，他的老婆人称顾大嫂，两个人的功夫都很厉害。顾大嫂有两个表兄弟叫解珍和解宝，他们是当地有名的猎人①。

一天，解珍和解宝发现了一只受伤的老虎，两个人赶紧追上去。老虎一边流②血一边跑，后来实在跑不动了，一下从山上滚了下去。老虎掉下去的地方正好是毛太公家的花园，解珍和解宝赶紧到毛太公家找老虎。

毛太公的儿子在自己家发现了老虎，就把它藏③了起来。

解珍和解宝到了毛太公家，请毛太公把老虎还

① 猎人 (lièrén) *n.* hunter
e.g., 我爷爷以前是一个猎人，还杀死过老虎呢。

② 流 (liú) *v.* (of liquid) flow
e.g., 你的鼻子怎么流血了？

③ 藏 (cáng) *v.* hide, conceal
e.g., 为了不让我吃糖，妈妈把家里的糖都藏起来了。

给他们。毛太公和他的儿子不仅没有把老虎还给解珍和解宝，还陷害他们，说解珍和解宝闯进自己家抢钱，把他们抓了起来送到官府。

顾大嫂知道解珍和解宝被抓了，赶紧找丈夫商量怎么救他们。

孙新说："毛太公家和官府的关系很好，官府肯定会帮助毛太公的。我们如果想救解珍和解宝，只能去监狱里把他们抢出来。可是监狱里面的士兵太多了，只凭我们两个，是没有办法救出他们的。我去找我哥哥帮忙。"

孙新的哥哥叫孙立，是登州的一个小官。孙新

① 里应外合
（lǐyìng-wàihé）
collaborate from
within with forces
from without
e.g., 他们里应外合,
终于打败了敌人。

把准备去监狱救解珍和解宝的事情告诉了孙立，孙立不想帮忙。

顾大嫂生气地对孙立说：“你可以不去，我们是一定要去的。等我们把解珍和解宝救出来，就逃到梁山去。官府如果抓不到我们，一定会去抓你。你就留下来等着被抓吧。”

孙立觉得顾大嫂说得有道理，只好答应帮忙。

第二天晚上，顾大嫂假装给解珍和解宝送饭，进到监狱里，和孙立 孙新里应外合①，顺利地救出了解珍和解宝。

孙立这些人离开监狱，又来到毛太公的家，把毛太公和他的儿子都杀

了，然后大家一起往<u>梁山</u>
逃去。

思考题：
Answer the following questions according to the story.

1. 解珍和解宝在登州从事什么职业？

2. 毛太公和他的儿子为什么陷害解珍和解宝？

3. 孙新和顾大嫂请谁帮忙，一起去监狱救解珍和解宝？

① 占领 (zhànlǐng) v.
capture, occupy
e.g., 我们的商品占
领了中国的大部分
市场。

② 打探 (dǎtàn) v.
probe information
about
e.g., 领导派我们打
探敌人的消息。

③ 打败 (dǎbài) v.
defeat
e.g., 这场比赛我们
打败了对手。

27. 宋江占领① 祝家庄

解珍、解宝、孙立、孙新和顾大嫂来到梁山的时候，宋江正准备第三次攻打祝家庄。

宋江前面两次攻打祝家庄都没有成功。这一次，孙立给宋江出了一个主意："我和祝家庄里教功夫的老师是好朋友，我可以去祝家庄找他，然后在祝家庄打探② 他们的情况，想办法帮助你们打败③ 祝家庄。"

宋江听了，十分高兴，同意了孙立的主意。

第二天，孙立带着孙新和顾大嫂，三个人假装是官府的人，来到祝家庄。

那个老师听到是孙立来了，十分高兴地问："你不是在登州当官吗，怎么来这里了？"

孙立说："登州知府把我派到郓城县，让我对付^①这些强盗。我经过祝家庄，来看看你。"

过了两天，宋江带着士兵继续攻打祝家庄，假装让孙立抓了石秀，目的是让祝朝奉信任孙立。果然，祝朝奉看见孙立抓了一个梁山的强盗，从此十分相信孙立。

这几天，孙立已经把祝家庄的情况打探清楚，他又找机会见到了被抓的石秀，让他随时准备行动。

又过了一天，祝朝奉的三个儿子带着大部分士兵去攻打宋江，只留下祝

① 对付 (duìfu) v.
deal with
e.g., 这些药是专门
用来对付老鼠的。

162

朝奉和孙立保护祝家庄。这个时候，祝家庄已经没有多少人了。

孙立趁祝朝奉不注意，把梁山的旗子插在了祝家庄的门口。梁山的人看见旗子，马上冲进祝家庄。孙新和顾大嫂来到监狱，救了被抓的石秀。

祝朝奉发现情况不好，正想逃走，被石秀发现了，石秀一刀杀了祝朝奉。祝朝奉的三个儿子也被李逵等人杀死了。

宋江占领祝家庄后，带着士兵回到梁山。

思考题：
Answer the following questions according to the story.

1. 孙立给宋江出了一个什么主意？
2. 祝朝奉为什么信任孙立？
3. 谁杀了祝朝奉？

28. 雷横得罪白秀英

主要人物和地点：

Main Characters and Places

白秀英（Bái Xiùyīng）：郓城县县令的情人。

Bai Xiuying: The mistress of the magistrate of Yuncheng County.

郓城县有一个叫雷横的小官，他很喜欢听戏。

一天，雷横来到戏院①听戏。一个叫白秀英的演员正在台上表演。白秀英唱②得很好，观众纷纷鼓掌称赞。

她表演完，拿出一个盘子，对观众说："如果大家喜欢我，就给我一些钱吧。"

雷横坐在戏院的最前面，白秀英首先来到他的旁边。

雷横伸手摸了摸衣服，发现没有带钱，只好跟白秀英解释，明天再给她钱。

白秀英不相信雷横没有带钱，她认为是雷横不想给她钱，就开始跟雷横吵架。

① 戏院 (xìyuàn) n. theater
e.g., 今天我们去戏院听京剧吧。

② 唱 (chàng) v. sing
e.g., 我喜欢听他唱歌，因为他唱得特别好听。

① 得罪 (dézuì) *v.*
offend, displease
e.g., 她做了很多得
罪人的事情。

② 伤 (shāng) *n.*
injury, wound
e.g., 他的伤还没有
好，所以要继续留
在医院。

这个时候，白秀英的父亲走了过来，也讽刺雷横是一个小气的人。

雷横再也忍不住了，朝白秀英的父亲打去。观众看见雷横打人，赶紧上去劝他，把雷横劝回了家。

那个白秀英是县令的女人，所以谁也不敢得罪① 她。白秀英看到父亲被雷横打了，哭着把这件事情告诉了县令。

县令听了白秀英的话，生气地命令士兵把雷横抓起来，捆在戏院门口，又给雷横的脖子戴上木枷 [1]。

雷横的母亲听说这件事，急忙来到戏院门口。她看见雷横的身上都是伤② ，伤心地哭了起来，一

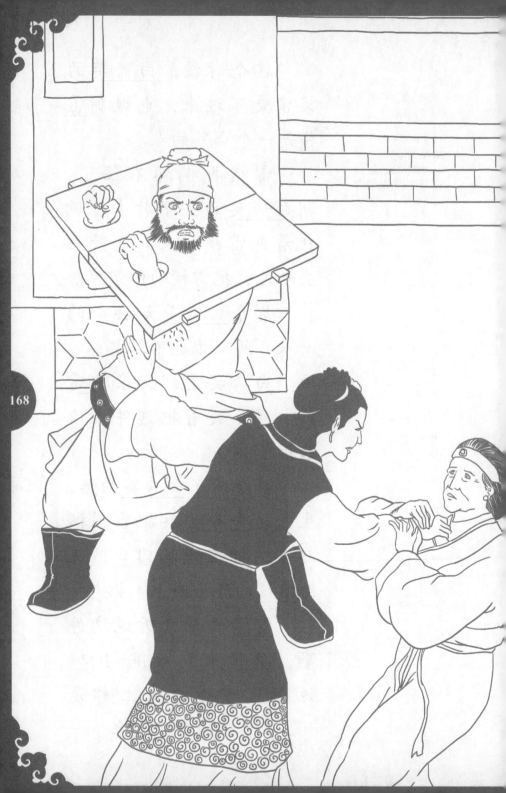

① 欺负 (qīfu) *v.* bully
e.g., 他总是欺负同学。

② 耳光 (ěrguāng) *n.*
slap in the face
e.g., 她生气地打了男朋友一个耳光。

边哭一边骂："这个白秀英欺负①我的儿子，她真是太坏了。"

白秀英在戏院里听到了雷横母亲的话，生气地走出来，打了雷横的母亲好几个耳光②，雷横的母亲差一点儿摔倒在地上。

雷横非常孝顺母亲。他看见母亲被白秀英打了，就使劲儿弄断了绳子，举起脖子上的木枷，朝白秀英的头打去，打死了白秀英。

县令听说白秀英死了，非常愤怒。他派朱仝把雷横押送到济州，准备在那里杀了雷横。

朱仝和雷横是好朋友，他押送雷横来到一片树林，悄悄对雷横说："你赶紧回家，带上母亲离开郓城县吧。"

雷横向朱仝表示感谢，然后带着母亲朝梁山逃去。

[1] 木枷（mùjiā）wooden yoke
中国古代套在犯人脖子上的一种刑具，一般用木板制成。
It referred to the collar worn around a prisoner's neck to confine him or her. It was usually made of wooden planks.

思考题：
Answer the following questions according to the story.

1. 雷横不给白秀英钱，是因为他不喜欢白秀英的演出吗？

2. 大家为什么不敢得罪白秀英？

3. 谁最后救了雷横？

29. 朱仝被逼上梁山

朱仝放走了雷横，所以被县令发配到沧州。沧州的知府派朱仝照顾自己四岁的小儿子。

一天晚上，朱仝带着小孩子在街道上玩。突然，他感觉有人在拉自己，转过身一看，竟然是雷横和吴用。

朱仝对小孩子说："我去给你买糖，你留下来等我，哪儿都不能去，知道吗？"

说完，朱仝拉着雷横和吴用走到人少的地方，问雷横："你怎么来了？"

雷横说："您救了我，宋江哥哥特别感谢您。他派我和吴用哥哥来沧州，接您去梁山。"

朱仝拒绝说："知府对我很好，我现在哪儿也不想去，只想做老百姓，过稳定的生活。"

朱仝坚决不答应去梁山，吴用只好对朱仝说："既然您不愿意去，那我们就不劝您了。"

朱仝赶紧回去找孩子，可是到处都找不到。

雷横对他说："别担心，可能是李逵把孩子抱走了。我们一起去找吧。"

三个人来到一个树林旁边，正好看见了李逵。

朱仝连忙问："小孩子呢？"

李逵说："他在树林里睡觉呢，你自己去找吧。"

朱仝跑到树林里，看见孩子躺在地上，已经死了。

朱仝生气极了，他冲出树林，愤怒地朝李逵大喊："你竟然杀了一个孩子，实在

是太残忍①了。"说完，朱仝就朝李逵扑去，要杀了李逵。

吴用急忙拦下朱仝，对他说："现在您要是回去了，知府肯定会杀了您。您跟我们走吧。"

朱仝想："知府要是知道儿子死了，一定会杀了我。我干脆就跟他们走吧。"

朱仝虽然②答应跟他们一起去梁山，可是因为李逵杀小孩子的事情，朱仝一直不跟李逵说话。

① 残忍 (cánrěn) adj. brutal, ruthless e.g., 你太残忍了，竟然杀了这只小猫。

② 虽然 (suīrán) conj. although, though e.g., 虽然我很努力，可是考试成绩还是不好。

174

思考题：
Answer the following questions according to the story.

1. 雷横为什么来沧州找朱仝？

2. 朱仝刚遇到雷横时，想去梁山吗？

3. 李逵为什么杀了知府的儿子？

30. 偷铠甲、骗徐宁

主要人物和地点：
Main Characters and Places

徐宁（Xú Níng）：擅长使用钩镰枪，他的钩镰枪法天下独步。他上梁山后教梁山好汉使用钩镰枪。

Xu Ning: Very skilled in using a hooked lance and unrivaled in lance skills. He instructed the Liangshan outlaws on how to use the hooked lance.

汤隆（Tāng Lóng）：徐宁的亲戚，负责梁山兵器铁甲的打造。

Tang Long: A relative of Xu Ning. He was responsible for making weapons and suits of armor at Liangshan.

时迁（Shí Qiān）：被誉为天下第一神偷。他练就一身好轻功，能飞檐走壁。

Shi Qian: Honored as the "best thief under heaven" for being extremely agile. He could even leap onto roofs and jump over walls.

东京有个叫徐宁的人，功夫很厉害，所以宋江很想请他来梁山，教大家功夫。

可是，如果徐宁不愿意来呢？

徐宁的亲戚汤隆正好也在梁山，他对大家说："徐宁很喜欢一副①铠甲[1]，只要偷了他的铠甲，我就有办法让他来梁山。"

于是宋江派时迁去徐宁的家里偷铠甲，又派汤隆配合时迁。

徐宁的铠甲放在一个红色的盒子里面。晚上的时候，时迁趁徐宁不注意，偷了这个盒子。

徐宁发现铠甲被偷了，非常伤心。

① 副 (fù) m.w. set
e.g., 他送给我一副眼镜。

第二天，汤隆来找徐宁，跟徐宁说："您的铠甲是不是丢了？我看见有个男人拿着一个红盒子，朝山东方向走了。"

徐宁听了，赶紧让汤隆带他去追那个人。

徐宁和汤隆追了两天，到了晚上，他们坐在一棵树下休息。

突然，汤隆叫了起来："你看！那个人不是背着一个红盒子吗？"

徐宁往汤隆指的方向看，果然看见时迁背着红盒子坐在树下。

徐宁立刻冲过去抓住时迁，生气地说："快把铠甲还给我。"

时迁连忙说："昨天晚

上我已经把铠甲卖了。你要是放了我，我就带你去找铠甲。"

于是，徐宁就跟着时迁一起去找铠甲。可是徐宁并不知道，时迁带着他一直在往梁山走去。

快到梁山的时候，时迁请徐宁喝了一碗有迷药的酒，徐宁喝完酒就晕倒在地上。大家赶紧把徐宁抬上车，继续向梁山走。

到了梁山，汤隆把事情都告诉了徐宁。原来，这一切都是汤隆安排的。他故意带徐宁去抓时迁，把徐宁骗到山东，然后又把徐宁弄晕，抬到梁山。

宋江把铠甲还给了徐宁，请求徐宁留在梁山，教大家功夫。

　　徐宁很佩服梁山的人，所以答应了宋江的请求，从此留在梁山。担任大家的功夫老师。

[1] 铠甲（kǎijiǎ）armor
古代军人打仗时穿的护身服装，多用金属片制成。
A protective covering for the body which was worn by soldiers in battles, usually made of sheet metal.

思考题：
Answer the following questions according to the story.

1. 宋江为什么想邀请徐宁来梁山？

2. 谁去徐宁家里偷的铠甲？

3. 徐宁是怎么被骗上梁山的？

31. 晁盖中箭去世

主要人物和地点：
Main Characters and Places

曾家五虎（Zēng Jiā Wǔ Hǔ）：曾头市首领曾弄的五个儿子，名字叫曾涂、曾密、曾索、曾魁、曾升。曾家在曾头市拥有军马过万，无人敢惹。

"Five Tigers of the Zeng Family": The five sons of Zeng Nong, named Zeng Tu, Zeng Mi, Zeng Suo, Zeng Kui and Zeng Sheng. The Zeng family had a large army of over ten thousand troops that no one dared stand against.

史文恭（Shǐ Wéngōng）：曾家五虎的老师，神勇无敌，箭术超群。

Shi Wengong: As the mentor of the "Five Tigers of the Zeng Family", Shi Wengong possessed remarkable martial arts and shooting skills.

曾头市（Zēngtóu Shì）：地名，位于山东省郓城县。

Zeng's Family Fortress: A place located in present-day Yuncheng County, Shandong Province.

梁山最大的首领叫晁盖，大家很尊重他。不过他有一个缺点，就是考虑问题不够周到。

一天，一个人来到梁山，对晁盖说："我很佩服梁山的英雄，想把一匹非常好的马送给您。可是在曾头市，这匹马被曾家五虎的老师史文恭抢走了。"

晁盖听了，十分生气。他亲自带着士兵攻打曾头市，要抢回那匹马。

在曾头市外，晁盖正准备冲过去打曾家五虎，被林冲拦住了。

林冲拿着武器跟曾家五虎打了起来，曾家五虎打不过林冲，带着人逃回了曾头市。

晁盖等了三天，可是曾家五虎再也不敢出来了。

第四天，两个和尚找到晁盖，对他说："我们知道曾家五虎住的地方在哪里，可以带着您去抓他们。"

晁盖听了非常高兴，可是林冲怀疑这两个和尚可能是曾家五虎派来骗晁盖的。

那两个和尚看见林冲怀疑他们，就说："我们是和尚，从来不会骗人。我们知道梁山英雄都是好人，所以才自愿来带路的。"

晁盖觉得和尚说得很有道理，就对林冲说："我相信他们的话。今天晚上我带着人去抓曾家五虎，你留在山上配合我的行动。"

① 偏僻 (piānpì) *adj.*
remote, secluded
e.g., 你的家太偏僻
了，都没有公共汽
车。

② 晚 (wǎn) *adj.* late
e.g., 太晚了，赶紧
睡觉吧。

③ 包围 (bāowéi) *v.*
besiege, surround
e.g., 敌人已经把我
们包围了，我们根
本逃不出去。

④ 毒 (dú) *n.* poison
e.g., 你要小心，这
把刀上有毒。

等到晚上，晁盖带着人跟着两个和尚进入曾头市。走了一会儿，来到一处十分偏僻①的森林。这个时候，两个和尚突然消失了。晁盖马上明白自己上当了。他赶紧命令士兵往回走，可是已经晚②了。

曾家五虎带着人将晁盖包围③起来，史文恭朝晁盖射出一支箭，正好射中晁盖的头。

林冲赶紧把晁盖救了出来，送回梁山。可是射中晁盖的箭上有毒④，晁盖的伤没有办法治疗。

晁盖快死的时候，对宋江说："以后谁抓了史文恭，谁就是梁山的首领。"说完，他就去世了。

1. 晁盖有什么缺点？

2. 两个和尚是怎么获得晁盖信任的？

3. 晁盖是怎么死的？

32. 吴用算卦骗卢俊义

主要人物和地点：
Main Characters and Places

卢俊义（Lú Jùnyì）：本书中的经典人物形象之一，人称
"玉麒麟"。他是大名府富商、大财主，后来成为梁山第二
首领。

Lu Junyi: One of the main characters in the novel who was
nicknamed Jade Kirin. He was a wealthy businessman from
Daming Prefecture in present-day Hebei Province. Lu later
ranked second among the outlaws.

大名府有一个叫卢俊义的人，功夫很厉害。

宋江想请卢俊义带领①士兵攻打曾头市，就派吴用和李逵去大名府，把卢俊义骗到梁山。

这一天，吴用装作算命先生[1]，李逵装作吴用的仆人②，两个人来到大名府。

卢俊义在路上遇到吴用，吴用对卢俊义说："我能通过算卦[2]知道一个人的未来。"

卢俊义就请吴用到自己家，向他询问自己的未来怎么样。

吴用对卢俊义说："您的未来很不好，马上就有生命危险。"

卢俊义急忙问："这个

① 带领 (dàilǐng) v. lead
e.g., 老师带领我们去公园玩。

② 仆人 (púrén) n. servant
e.g., 公主让仆人拿着她的包。

188

卦金一兩
卜卦
請命談天

危险能避免吗？"

吴用说："这很容易，只要您离开大名府，躲到东南方向一千里外，就可以保证您的平安。"

接着，吴用又对卢俊义说："我有一首诗，写的内容就是您的未来，我来念，您可以把这首诗写在墙上，等危险发生了，再看看我说的是不是真的。"

这首诗是：

芦花丛里一扁舟，

俊杰俄从此地游。

义士若能知此理，

反躬逃难可无忧。[3]

吴用看卢俊义在墙上写完诗，就带着李逵离开了卢俊义家，往梁山走去。

李逵不太明白地问：

① 做客 (zuòkè) v.
be a guest
e.g., 这个周末我要
去朋友家里做客。

"你只跟卢俊义说了几句话，他就会来梁山？"

吴用说："那当然。我让他去东南方向一千里外，正好经过梁山。只要他到了那里，我们就把他骗进梁山。卢俊义家里的墙上写的诗，把每句话的第一个字连起来读，就是'卢俊义反'。谋反是死罪，官府一定会杀了他，所以他只能留在咱们梁山了。"

过了几天，卢俊义离开大名府，往东南方向走去。经过梁山的时候，宋江请卢俊义去梁山做客①。

卢俊义没有办法拒绝，只好在梁山住了几天。不过他不愿意做强盗，一直想离开梁山。

[1] 算命先生（suànmìng xiānsheng）fortune teller

算命先生是一个职业。他们通过算卦，推算出一个人的命运，断定这个人的吉凶祸福。

Fortune tellers attempt to predict one's future or tell one's fortune through techniques such as palm reading and Eight Trigrams principles.

[2] 算卦（suànguà）tell sb's fortune

算卦是一种利用个人切身资讯，例如脸与手的纹路、出生日期、姓名笔画等，配合五行和八卦，预测或推断行事是否顺利和命运吉凶福祸的行为。

It is the practice of predicting certain aspects of a person's life through the lines on their faces and hands, their birth dates, the number of strokes in their names, etc. Fortune telling was often practiced using the five elements theory and *bagua* (Eight Trigrams) principles.

[3] 芦花丛里一扁舟，俊杰俄从此地游。义士若能知此理，反躬逃难可无忧。

（Lúhuā cóng li yì piānzhōu, jùnjié é cóng cǐ dì yóu. Yìshì ruò néng zhī cǐ lǐ, fǎngōng táonàn kě wú yōu.）

这首诗的意思是"芦花丛中有一只小船，你不久将要从这里划船游过。倘若你知道这里面暗藏的道理，主动逃走，那就不用忧虑了"。这首诗每句话的第一个字连起来读就是"卢俊义反"，意思是"卢俊义要谋反"。吴用写这首诗的目的是陷害卢俊义，告诉大家卢俊义要谋反，逼卢俊义留在梁山。

It is an acrostic poem, in which the first character of each line forms the phrase 卢俊义反, meaning Lu Junyi is going to plot a rebellion. Wu Yong wrote the poem to frame Lu Junyi in order to force him to join the Liangshan outlaws.

思考题：

Answer the following questions according to the story.

1. 宋江为什么想请卢俊义来梁山？

2. 吴用为什么认为卢俊义一定会上梁山？

3. 卢俊义最后相信吴用算的卦了吗？

33. 燕青救卢俊义

主要人物和地点:
Main Characters and Places

燕青（Yān Qīng）：被称作"浪子"，卢俊义的心腹。文武双全，箭法出众，能百步穿杨，后来跟随卢俊义一起加入梁山。

Yan Qing: Yan Qing was nicknamed the "Wanderer". As a trusted subordinate of Lu Junyi, he was both a powerful fighter and a talented musician. Yan Qing was also adept at arrow shooting. He joined Liangshan with Lu Junyi.

沙门岛（Shāmén Dǎo）：一座海岛，位于今山东省庙岛群岛。北宋时，沙门岛是流放、囚禁犯了重罪的人的地方。

Shamen Island: An island located in the Miaodao Island chain in Shandong Province. During the Northern Song Dynasty (960-1127), Shamen Island was where criminals charged with a serious crime were exiled and imprisoned.

卢俊义不愿意留在梁山，宋江只好让他回家。

卢俊义有一个仆人叫燕青，他射箭的功夫很厉害。

卢俊义在回家的路上遇到燕青。燕青哭着说："您刚刚离开家，您的妻子和管家[1]就去官府陷害您当了强盗。现在他们已经结婚了，还把我从家里赶出来。我劝您还是回梁山吧，您如果回家，肯定会被官府抓起来。"

卢俊义不相信燕青的话，燕青只好伤心地离开卢俊义。

卢俊义到了家，他的妻子和管家很吃惊，先假装高兴地欢迎他回家，然后悄悄离开家，去官府报告卢俊义回来了。

过了一会儿，衙役来到卢俊义家，把他抓到官府。

那个管家对知府说："卢俊义在墙上写了一首诗，每句话的第一个字连起来，就是'卢俊义反'。这可以证明卢俊义是强盗。"

知府派人去卢俊义的家里检查，发现真的有这首诗，于是相信了卢俊义是强盗，把卢俊义发配到沙门岛。

这个时候，卢俊义才相信燕青的话，他的妻子和管家真的陷害他。

卢俊义的妻子和管家还是不放心，他们找到押送卢俊义去沙门岛的两个衙役，给了这两个衙役很多钱，请衙役在路上杀了卢俊义。

这两个衙役看见钱，连忙答应了管家。

在去沙门岛的路上，两个衙役带着卢俊义来到一片树林，准备在这里杀了卢俊义。

突然，两支箭从树上射下来，把那两个衙役给杀死了。

这个时候，燕青从树上跳下来，抱着卢俊义哭着说："我一直跟着您，想找机会救您。刚才看到那两个衙役想杀您，我就把他们都杀了。"

卢俊义说："我们再也

不能回<u>大名府</u>了，现在还
能去哪儿呢？"

　　<u>燕青</u>说："我们现在只
能去<u>梁山</u>了。"说完，他就
背着<u>卢俊义</u>朝<u>梁山</u>走去。

[1] 管家（guǎnjiā）steward
在中国古代，管家指地位较高的仆人，他们专门为地主和官僚管理家产和日
常事务。
In ancient China, it is a servant of high position, who handles the management of properties and daily business for landlords and bureaucrats.

思考题：
Answer the following questions according to the story.

1. 是谁向官府报告卢俊义回家的？

2. 官府为什么相信卢俊义当了强盗？

3. 燕青用什么方法救了卢俊义？

① 进入 (jìnrù) v.
enter
e.g., 他进入图书馆
借书。

34. 宋江攻打大名府

在去梁山的路上，卢俊义又被官府的人抓住了。燕青只好去梁山报告这个消息。

宋江知道卢俊义被抓了，十分着急。

吴用说："哥哥不用着急，我们正好趁这个机会攻打大名府，不仅可以救出卢俊义，还可以抢到大名府的粮食。"

宋江同意了吴用的建议。

吴用先派时迁悄悄进入①大名府，等到元宵节[1]的晚上，在大名府里放火。接着，吴用又命令林冲、徐宁、李逵和雷横等人带着士兵，分别等在大名府的四个门外，一旦看见大名府里着火，就一起攻打大名府的四个门。

到了元宵节的晚上，时迁进入大名府，来到一个没有人注意的地方，开始放火。过了一会儿，大火就燃烧起来了。

这个时候，街道上有人喊："不好了，梁山的士兵已经把大名府包围了，马上就要攻打大名府了。"大名府的老百姓十分害怕，纷纷逃回家里。

大名府外的林冲等人，看见大名府着火了，马上开始攻打这个城市的大门。官府的士兵急忙报告大名府的知府梁中书。

梁中书正在家里欣赏月亮，忽然听到有人喊："梁山攻打大名府了。"他

十分害怕，连忙骑上马，带着一些士兵准备逃出大名府。

可是大名府东、西、南、北①四个方向的大门都有梁山士兵。梁中书只好一边到处躲藏，一边寻找可以离开大名府的路。幸亏有士兵的保护，梁中书才逃出大名府。

宋江带领士兵占领了大名府，大家打开②监狱的门，救出了卢俊义，还把卢俊义的管家杀死了。

他们把大名府的粮食分成两部分，一部分分给老百姓，一部分带回梁山。

① 北 (běi) *n.* north
e.g., 你往北走就能找到图书馆。

② 打开 (dǎkāi) *v.* open
e.g., 你能把窗户打开吗？

[1] 元宵节（Yuánxiāo Jié）Lantern Festival
农历正月十五的元宵节是中国的传统节日，吃元宵、赏花灯、猜灯谜、观满月是几项重要的元宵节民间习俗。

It is a traditional festival in China which falls on the 15th day of the first lunar month of the Chinese New Year. The main folk activities during this festival include eating *yuanxiao* (sweet stuffed dumplings made of glutinous rice flour and served in soup), watching lantern shows, solving lantern riddles and appreciating the full moon.

思考题：
Answer the following questions according to the story.

1. 宋江为什么要攻打大名府？

2. 梁山派谁在大名府放火？

3. 梁山是怎么处理大名府的粮食的？

35. 卢俊义抓史文恭

主要人物和地点：
Main Characters and Places

曾弄（Zēng Nòng）：曾头市的主人。他有五个儿子，分别是曾涂、曾密、曾索、曾魁、曾升，被称作曾家五虎。

Zeng Nong: The headman of Zeng's Family Fortress. His five sons Zeng Tu, Zeng Mi, Zeng Suo, Zeng Kui and Zeng Sheng were known as the "Five Tigers of the Zeng Family".

① 出战 (chūzhàn) v.
go into battle
e.g., 这次跑步比赛，
你们派谁出战啊？

晁盖在攻打曾头市的时候，被史文恭用箭射死了。后来，史文恭又派人连续两次抢了梁山的马。

宋江实在忍不住了，决定亲自带人攻打曾头市。

曾头市的主人曾弄派大儿子、小儿子和史文恭出战①。可是梁山的人实在太厉害了，两个儿子都被杀死了。

曾弄失去了两个儿子，非常伤心。他害怕其余三个儿子也被杀死，就叫史文恭给宋江写信，他不想再继续打了。

宋江收到信，看见信上只是写着"我们愿意把抢来的马还给你"，没有道歉的话，就生气地说："他

205

们杀了晁盖哥哥，居然连道歉都没有。"

吴用也读了信，他悄悄地对宋江说了几句话。宋江听了很开心，连忙给曾弄写信，同意不再继续打了。不过，宋江要求曾弄除了还马，还要把抢马的人也送到梁山。

曾弄和史文恭同意了宋江的要求，他们把马和抢马的人都交给了宋江。

宋江把抢马的人叫来，说："我有事情需要你帮忙，如果成功了，我就放了你。"那个人马上答应了。

宋江让他假装逃回曾头市，对史文恭说："宋江现在只想把马要回去，根

本不关心其他的事情。如果我们今天晚上去攻打他们，一定会成功的。"

史文恭听了，一点儿也没有怀疑。他赶紧让所有的人都做好准备，晚上去攻打宋江的军营①。

晚上，史文恭带着人冲进了宋江的军营，可是军营里一个人也没有。史文恭知道自己被宋江骗了。他刚要跑，梁山的人就冲了出来。他们把曾弄的三个儿子全杀了。史文恭的马跑得很快，他逃进了树林。

卢俊义和燕青正在树林里等着史文恭。史文恭打不过卢俊义和燕青，被他们抓住了。

① 军营 (jūnyíng) *n.* military camp e.g., 我家附近有一个军营，里面住着三百多个士兵。

1. 宋江为什么决定亲自带兵攻打曾头市？
2. 曾弄为什么不想继续跟宋江打了？
3. 宋江给史文恭和曾弄的信里，同意不再继续攻打曾头市的条件是什么？

209

36. 众多英雄聚梁山

主要人物和地点：
Main Characters and Places

东平府（Dōngpíng Fǔ）：中国古代的地名，位于今山东省东平县。

Dongping Prefecture: A place in ancient China located in present-day Dongping County, Shandong Province.

东昌府（Dōngchāng Fǔ）：中国古代的地名，位于今山东省聊城市。

Dongchang Prefecture: A place in ancient China located in present-day Liaocheng, Shandong Province.

忠义堂（Zhōngyì Táng）：梁山英雄商议军情、调兵遣将的地方。忠义堂有一百零八个位置，表示梁山一共有一百零八位首领。

Hall of Loyalty and Righteousness: The operational headquarters of Liangshan. There were 108 seats in the hall representing the 108 heroes.

宋江让人在晁盖的灵位[1]前面杀死了史文恭，然后把大家叫来，说："大家应该还记得，晁盖哥哥死的时候曾经说'谁抓了史文恭，谁就当梁山的首领！'今天卢俊义抓了史文恭，应该让他当首领。"

卢俊义赶紧拒绝说："不行，不行，我不能当首领。大家愿意让我留在梁山，我已经很高兴了。"

宋江说："不是我谦虚，是我实在不如您。您应该做梁山的首领。"

卢俊义听完，急忙跪下说："哥哥您不要再说了，我不会当首领的。"

吴用本来也不愿意让

卢俊义当首领，担心他没有能力管理梁山，于是吴用对宋江说："宋江哥哥当第一首领，卢俊义当第二首领。如果您再不愿意当首领，恐怕会让大家伤心。"

李逵也已经忍不住了，吴用刚说完，他就对宋江喊："大家都希望你当首领。你要是再拒绝，大家不如就散伙①吧。"

其他人也跟着李逵一起劝宋江。最后，宋江说："我有一个主意。有两个地方我一直想攻打，一个是东平府，一个是东昌府。我和卢俊义带着士兵各自攻打一个地方，谁先获得胜利谁就当首领。"

大家都同意了。宋江

① 散伙 (sànhuǒ) v. dissolve, disband e.g., 我们散伙吧，这个公司开不下去了。

① 聚 (jù) v. gather,
assemble
e.g., 大家聚在一起
商量一下这个问题。

② 石碑 (shíbēi) n.
stone tablet
e.g., 那个地方有一
块儿巨大的石碑。

带人攻打<u>东平府</u>，<u>卢俊义</u>带人攻打<u>东昌府</u>。

结果，<u>宋江</u>先获得了胜利，当了<u>梁山</u>的首领。

<u>宋江</u>正式做首领的那一天，大家都来到<u>忠义堂</u>，按照各自在<u>梁山</u>的地位坐下，正好是一百零八个人。

<u>宋江</u>非常高兴地说："今天，我们一百零八个兄弟聚①在<u>梁山</u>，我非常高兴。我想做一块石碑②，刻上大家的名字，大家觉得怎么样？"

所有人都同意了。

从此，<u>梁山</u>发展得更快了。他们继续抢坏人的钱，再把钱分给老百姓，老百姓都很喜欢他们。

[1] 灵位（língwèi）memorial tablet

人死后，亲朋好友在房间里暂时摆放一个木牌，上面写着死者的名字，这就是灵位。灵位是用来供奉死者的。

A wooden board with the name of the deceased carved into it, which was placed in a special room temporarily for the purposes of prayer and worship by friends and relatives.

思考题：
Answer the following questions according to the story.

1. 按照晁盖死前说的话，梁山的首领应该是谁？

2. 最后谁当了梁山的首领？

3. 梁山总共有多少位英雄？

1. Lu Da and Butcher Zheng

There was once a man named Lu Da in the city of Weizhou who was tall and stout. As someone who was always ready to help those in need, Lu Da tended to act impetuously.

One day, Lu Da was having a drink with his friends at a pub. Suddenly, they heard a whimper.

Lu Da angrily asked the waiter, "Who is bringing our mood down?" Then, the waiter brought to him a young lady and an old man who were crying.

Lu Da asked them, "Why are you crying?"

The young lady said, "My name is Jin Cuilian. I came to Weizhou with my father to look for our relatives. There is a man nicknamed Zhenguanxi (Butcher Zheng) here who forced me to become his concubine while promising some money to my father. However, upon marrying into his family, I was driven out by his wife. Now, he is asking for the money back which he had never given my father. We are crying because we have no money to give him."

Hearing this, Lu Da was filled with anger and said to the girl, "Don't be afraid! I will give you some money and you should leave Weizhou as soon as possible. Let me find this man and teach him a lesson!"

After seeing the girl and her father off, Lu Da went to look for Butcher Zheng right away.

Butcher Zheng ran a butcher shop. He slaughtered pigs and sold the pork. He greeted Lu Da and asked, "What can I do for you?"

Lu Da replied, "I want you to cut ten *jin* of minced lean meat, which should not contain any single bit of fat; then I want ten *jin* of minced fat meat, which should not contain any single bit of lean meat."

Butcher Zheng was kept busy the whole morning preparing this peculiar order. After he finished, he wrapped the meat up and handed it to Lu Da.

Lu Da then added, "I also want ten *jin* of gristle, which should not have any bit of meat on it."

Butcher Zheng got angry, "Are you here to make a fool of me?"

Lu Da flung all the meat onto Zheng's face and said, "You're right! That's exactly what I'm here for! To make a fool of you!"

Butcher Zheng couldn't control his temper anymore. In a fury, he grabbed his big butcher knife to hack Lu Da.

Lu Da kicked him down to the ground, beating him up while scolding, "You have to pay the price for cheating Jin Cuilian!"

In tears, Butcher Zheng begged for mercy, to which Lu Da turned a deaf ear. After being fiercely beaten for some time, Zheng was no longer uttering a sound.

Lu Da thought, "My goodness! Is he dead?" Lu Da was afraid of being caught, so he deliberately said to the butcher, "Don't pretend to be dead, I will come again to give you another lesson!" Then he fled right away.

2. Monk Lu Causing Trouble on Mount Wutai

After killing Butcher Zheng, Lu Da found shelter on Mount Wutai and became a monk, where he was given the religious name Zhishen (Monk Lu). Monks were forbidden from drinking alcohol and eating meat, which was unbearable for him.

One day, Monk Lu wanted to buy some liquor, but the vendor said, "Monks are not supposed to drink liquor, I can't sell it to you."

Monk Lu angrily seized the liquor jar and drank it in one gulp. He then told the vendor, "Come to my temple tomorrow to pick up the money."

Monk Lu got drunk and stumbled his way to the temple. Two monks saw him and said angrily, "As a monk, how could you indulge yourself in alcohol?"

Then, the two monks gathered more than 20 people to capture him. Monk Lu grabbed a wooden club and let out a loud cry, which frightened the crowd. They all took several steps back.

Learning about this, the abbot rushed to the scene to stop him, "Zhishen, put the club down!" The abbot censured Monk Lu and warned him never to take up drinking or beating others again.

Monk Lu had a deep respect for the abbot so that he put the club down and readily accepted his request.

A few days later, Monk Lu went to a blacksmith to cast a monk's staff that would weigh over 100 *jin*.

After leaving the shop, he arrived at a pub for a drink and some meat. Seeing that Lu was a monk, the owner told him, "The meat has sold out."

Monk Lu didn't believe the pub owner, so he went to the kitchen himself and found some meat and liquor. He then began eating it joyously.

After finishing drinking, Monk Lu wrapped whatever meat was left and told the owner, "I'll come back tomorrow." The owner had to agree.

Upon returning to the temple, Monk Lu suddenly felt sick and threw up everything he just ate. When the other monks saw some meat in his vomit and discovered that he had consumed alcohol again, they became furious and started fighting with him. They didn't stop until the abbot arrived.

The next day, the abbot called Monk Lu in and gave him some money. He told him, "You have violated the provisions time and time again, so I can't allow you to stay here any longer. I will write a letter and introduce you to the Xiangguo Temple in the capital Dongjing."

Departing from the temple, Monk Lu went to the blacksmith to pick up the monk's staff. He then embarked on his journey to Dongjing.

3. Lu Zhishen at Peach Blossom Manor

It had been over half a month since Lu Zhishen left on his journey to the Xiangguo Temple in Dongjing. One evening, he was passing by the Peach Blossom Manor, where he decided to spend the night at Squire Liu's residence.

Squire Liu warned Lu Zhishen, "Don't go outside tonight."

Lu Zhishen asked in surprise, "Why?"

Squire Liu seemed to be angry and said, "This evening, my

daughter will get married."

Lu Zhishen asked him with a smile, "That's an auspicious event, why do you seem unhappy?"

Squire Liu answered, "There is a bandit named Zhou Tong who is forcing me to marry my daughter to him."

Lu Zhishen said, "I'll go talk to him about giving up the thought of marrying your daughter."

Lu Zhishen decided to teach Zhou Tong a lesson. Disguised as Liu's daughter, he waited for Zhou in the chamber. There was no light in the room, so when Zhou Tong walked in, he took Lu Zhishen who was sitting on the bed as Liu's daughter and began touching "her". Suddenly, he was struck by Lu Zhishen.

Zhou Tong asked in astonishment, "How can you beat your husband?"

Lu Zhishen threw Zhou Tong to the ground and said, "Take a closer look at 'your wife'!"

Zhou Tong cried for help immediately, "Help, help!" The bandits rushed into the chamber to save their boss. Lu Zhishen grabbed his monk's staff and fought against the bandits. As the bandits ran away, Zhou took the chance and fled.

Squire Liu burst into tears and said, "You defeated Zhou Tong! Now the bandits will come back and kill us!"

Lu Zhishen comforted him, "Don't be afraid. I will deal with them."

After some time, a shout was suddenly heard, "The chief of bandits is coming with all his men!"

Lu Zhishen said, "Let me have a look."He went outside with the monk's staff.

The chief was on a horse, shouting toward the house, "Where's the monk? Come out now!"

Lu Zhishen walked to him and replied, "I'm right here."

Upon seeing him, the chief burst into laughter and asked, "Don't you recognize me, sir?"

Lu Zhishen took a closer look at the chief's face, and found that he was none other than Li Zhong, his good friend.

Li Zhong invited Lu Zhishen to his home to have a chat; Lu agreed. Upon their arrival, Zhou Tong saw Lu Zhishen and asked Li Zhong in anger, "Brother, why have you brought this monk to our home?"

Li Zhong replied, "Do you know who he is? He is Lu Zhishen!"

Zhou Tong was very surprised, "What? He is indeed Lu Zhishen! Thank God I wasn't beaten to death by him!"

Lu Zhishen stayed at Li's residence for a few days. He then left the Peach Blossom Manor and continued his journey to Dongjing.

4. Lu Zhishen and the Willow Tree

After another eight or nine days, Lu Zhishen finally arrived at Xiangguo Temple. A monk led Lu Zhishen to meet the abbot.

Lu Zhishen showed the letter to the abbot. The abbot thus learned about his wrongdoings on Mount Wutai and became worried that Lu might cause more trouble at Xiangguo Temple. He didn't want Lu Zhishen to stay but didn't know how to decline.

At this moment, a monk made a suggestion, "I remember there is a vegetable plot in our temple; the vegetables there were often stolen. Lu Zhishen can be lodged there to take care of the plot." The abbot agreed.

Two men named Zhang San and Li Si often came to the plot in Xiangguo Temple to steal vegetables. They decided to give Lu Zhishen a lesson, so he wouldn't have the guts to watch over the plot.

One day, the two gathered more than ten people to where Lu Zhishen was lodged. They knelt down beside the manure pit. Lu Zhishen was surprised to see this, so he went over to help.

As Lu Zhishen was getting close, one of them suddenly clinched his legs and tried to push him into the pit.

To everyone's surprise, Zhang San and Li Si were kicked into the manure pit by Lu Zhishen instead with a loud splash. The others all got so frightened that they fell to their knees and didn't dare to move a bit. Lu Zhishen burst into laughter and gave them a harsh rebuke.

The next day, Zhang San and Li Si visited Lu Zhishen and invited him for dinner to offer their apology. As they were eating, drinking and chatting under a big willow tree, a crow suddenly cried out. One of them then wanted to climb up the tree and drive the crow away.

Lu Zhishen said, "Look, this is how I drive the crow away." He walked to the willow, clinched the trunk, then exerted himself and pulled the big tree out of the ground.

Zhang San and Li Si were so astounded that they knelt down and praised, "You have such amazing strength, master!"

However, Lu Zhishen said, "That's nothing. Let me show you my real strength!" He then picked up his monk's staff and began demonstrating his skills of martial arts, stunning everybody.

At that moment, a loud cheer was heard from outside, "Fantastic skills!"

Lu Zhishen looked out and saw a man in his mid-thirties. He asked Zhang San and Li Si, "Who is that guy?"

Li Si replied, "He is the martial arts instructor of the 800,000 imperial guards. His name is Lin Chong."

Delighted, Lu Zhishen rushed toward Lin Chong and introduced himself, "I am Lu Zhishen, I met your father when I was a child."

Lin Chong was also very pleased and addressed Lu Zhishen as "elder brother". The two sat down to enjoy a drink together and became good friends.

5. Lin Chong and the White Tiger Hall

There was a playboy named Master Gao in Dongjing. He did all kinds of bad deeds but no one dared to discipline him since he was the adopted son of Grand Marshal Gao, a very high-ranking official.

One day, Master Gao came across Lin Chong's wife. Enchanted by her beauty, he began harboring the idea of taking her as his own. However, he wasn't brave enough to take any actions given the strength of her husband.

Lu Qian, Lin Chong's friend, had always wanted to curry favor with Master Gao and Grand Marshal Gao. When discovering Master Gao was upset about being unable to get close to Lin's wife, he came up with an idea.

A few days later, Lu Qian invited Lin Chong out for dinner while sending someone to Lin Chong's residence to tell his wife, "Your husband suddenly fell ill and tumbled to the ground. Please go and take a look!"

Lin's wife rushed to Lu Qian's house with her maid, but found no trace of her husband. It was Master Gao who was expecting her. She immediately sent the maid to inform Lin Chong, who arrived in time and beat Gao away.

Feeling disappointed and scared, Master Gao fell ill after he got back home.

The Grand Marshal didn't have a son, and Gao was his only adopted son. So the Grand Marshal loved him dearly. Seeing that his son was confined to the sickbed, Gao became very worried.

Lu Qian suggested to Grand Marshal Gao, "Your son will recover if we kill Lin Chong and seize his wife." The two then tried to think of a way to have Lin Chong killed.

A few days later, Lin Chong came across a sword-seller on the street. He found it was quite a nice sword and immediately bought it.

The next day, two men came to look for Lin Chong. They told him, "We heard that you just bought a treasured sword. Grand Marshal Gao would like to see it." Lin Chong had to agree.

They took Lin Chong to a hall in Grand Marshal Gao's residence and asked him to stay there. Then they left.

Feeling surprised, Lin Chong started to look around the hall. When he looked up, he saw some Chinese characters in large print above the gate, "White Tiger Hall". The hall was a place of great importance where no one could enter without Grand Marshal Gao's permission. Anyone who violated such a provision would be sentenced to death.

Lin Chong was shocked to see this. Before he could even turn around to leave, Grand Marshal Gao appeared. He said to Lin Chong furiously, "How come you entered the White Tiger Hall with a sword? Do you want to kill me?"

Lin Chong explained, "I was brought here by your men, Grand Marshal."

Gao replied, "That's nonsense! I didn't ask anyone to send for you."

Lin Chong was arrested and sent to the local government office.

The government officials showed great sympathy to him. They came up with an idea: Change his charge of "breaking into the White Tiger Hall presumptuously" into "entering the hall by mistake", in order to make the point that Lin Chong did not enter on purpose. Thanks to that, Lin Chong was not given a death sentence; instead, he was banished to Cangzhou while being escorted by two guards, Xue Ba and Dong Chao.

6. Lu Zhishen in the Wild Boar Woods

Learning that Lin Chong wasn't given a death sentence, Grand Marshal Gao came up with another scheme to kill him. He sent some money to Xue Ba and Dong Chao, the two escorting guards, asking them to end Lin Chong's life on the way to Cangzhou. Xue and Dong accepted the offer right away.

During the journey, Xue Ba and Dong Chao constantly beat Lin Chong up. Lin's feet were also badly burned by them.

One evening, they reached the Wild Boar Woods. It was a very dangerous place seldom visited by people. Xue Ba said, "I'm too tired to walk any further."

"Me too," said Dong Chao.

Hearing that, Lin Chong sat down against a big tree. Unexpectedly, Xue Ba and Dong Chao took out a rope and tied him up.

Xue Ba told Lin Chong, "It's Grand Marshal Gao's order. We have to obey him."

Just as Xue Ba was about to kill Lin Chong, a stout monk jumped out from behind a tree. It was none other than Lu Zhishen. He held his monk's staff up to kill Xue Ba and Dong Chao. Lin Chong stopped him and said, "It's Grand Marshal Gao's order. How dare they disobey him? Just let them go."

Lu Zhishen then took out a knife and cut the rope to set Lin Chong free. He then told Lin, "After I heard that you were being escorted to Cangzhou, I've been following you just in case some help might be needed. I reckon that they may kill you in the Wild Boar Woods and so I've arrived here early to protect you."

Lu Zhishen found a carriage for Lin Chong so he didn't have to walk on his burned feet and could rest a little. Out of fear of the ferocious monk, Xue Ba and Dong Chao dared not express any objections.

Lu Zhishen accompanied Lin Chong for more than ten days until Lin Chong's feet nearly recovered.

One day, Lu Zhishen said to Lin Chong, "We will arrive in Cangzhou soon and I won't company you anymore. I've checked out this place. There are people living nearby. You can rest assured that they wouldn't dare harm you."

Lu Zhishen then gave Lin Chong some money. He warned Xue Ba and Dong Chao while pointing at a big tree, "If you ever hurt my brother again, you will end up like this tree!" He then held up his staff and cut down the tree with just one hack.

Dong Chao was astounded, "This monk is truly amazing!"

Lin Chong replied, "That's nothing. At Xiangguo Temple, he pulled out a big willow tree from the ground single-handedly!"

Only then did Xue Ba and Dong Chao realize that monk was Lu Zhishen from Xiangguo Temple.

7. Lin Chong Seeking Shelter

After being escorted to Cangzhou by Xue Ba and Dong Chao, Lin Chong was put in jail. Xue and Dong returned to Dongjing to report to Grand Marshal Gao about their failure in killing Lin Chong.

Gao then dispatched Lu Qian to Cangzhou in another attempt to take Lin's life.

Upon arriving in Cangzhou, Lin Chong was assigned by the prison officer to oversee a fodder depot in the eastern part of the city. Heavy snow began to fall when he arrived at the depot with a minor official, who handed him the key to the gate and left.

Alone in the fodder depot, Lin Chong felt rather cold. So, he walked to a pub and bought some meat and liquor. As soon as he returned to the depot, he found his hut was weighed down by the snow. It was still snowing heavily. Lin Chong had to seek shelter somewhere else. He then remembered he saw a temple on his way back from the pub. So, he took his weapon and quilt to spend the night there.

After a while, Lin Chong suddenly noticed the fodder depot was on fire! When he was about to rush over and put the fire out, he detected three men were approaching the temple, but they were unable to push the gate open because Lin Chong locked it with a rock. They instead stood outside the temple.

One man said to the other, "Thank you for your help! I'll report this to Grand Marshal Gao. He will surely give you a promotion!"

The other man said, "I climbed into the fodder depot and set fire at four or five spots. Lin Chong must be dead by now."

The third man replied, "Later we shall go back there to pick some of his bones. I will take them back to Grand Marshal Gao."

Lin Chong could clearly discern that the three men outside the temple were none other than Lu Qian, one subordinate of Gao Qiu and the official who brought him to the depot. He became furious and thought, "I'm so lucky the hut had collapsed, or else I must have been dead by now!"

He quietly pushed the rock away, then dashed out from the temple with his sword. After killing the depot official and Gao's subordinate, Lin Chong approached Lu Qian, kicking him down to the ground. Terrified, Lu Qian begged for mercy, "Please don't kill me!"

Lin Chong asked, "There is no hatred between us, but why are you trying to kill me? "

Lu Qian replied with fear, "I didn't mean to kill you! I was ordered by Grand Marshal Gao to do it! I'm not involved!"

Lin Chong yelled angrily, "I've long been treating you as a friend, but now you are trying to take my life! How come you are not involved?"

Saying so, he killed Lu Qian with his sword.

Knowing that he had committed a serious crime by killing the three, Lin Chong dared not stay in Cangzhou any longer. Having heard that there was a group of outlaws at Liangshan, he made up his mind to go there and join them.

8. Yang Zhi Selling His Treasured Sword

There was a man named Yang Zhi who excelled in martial arts. He went to Dongjing with a lot of money in the hope of buying an official post there.

Yang Zhi had spent almost all the money after just a few days, but still failed in obtaining a post. Out of despair, he headed for the market to sell the treasured sword left to him by his elders just to get some money for food.

At the market, Yang Zhi was holding the sword and waiting for an offer from the customers. A drunken hooligan called Niu Er stumbled up to him and asked, "How much is your sword?"

Yang Zhi replied, "3,000 strings of coins."

Niu Er said, "That's too expensive!"

Yang Zhi replied, "This is the best of its kind. Firstly, it can cut copper coins without any damage to itself; secondly, if you blow some hair onto its blade, the hair will be cut in half; thirdly, no blood is left on it after it kills someone."

Niu Er then took out 20 copper coins and piled them up, one on top of the other, asking Yang Zhi to hack them with his sword. With one single hack, all of the coins were cut into half. All the onlookers cheered at this marvel.

Niu Er shouted in anger, "That's nothing!" He then plucked a tuft of hair from his own head and asked Yang Zhi to cut it with the sword. Yang Zhi held the hair in hand, blew it onto the blade, the hair was then cut in half with the light blow. People cheered again in excitement!

Niu Er got even more angry. He challenged Yangzhi, "I don't believe no blood will be left on the sword once a person is killed with it. Kill someone to prove it to me!"

Yang Zhi said, "I can show you by killing a dog."

Niu Er cursed, "You told us no blood will be left on your sword once a person is killed, not a dog!"

Yang Zhi was annoyed, "Go away if you don't want to buy the sword. Don't disturb my business!"

Niu Er refused to leave and challenged Yang Zhi again, "Do you have the guts to kill me?"

Feeling furious, Yang Zhi wanted to leave with his sword but was stopped by Niu Er, who persisted, "Don't go! Kill me if you dare!" He then tried to fight Yang Zhi.

Out of anger, Yang Zhi killed Niu Er right away with the sword and then gave himself up to the government office.

At the government office, Yang Zhi made a confession of guilt. The official thought Yang was indeed very capable; furthermore, the man he killed was a well-known hooligan, so he didn't give Yang Zhi a death sentence. Instead, Yang would be exiled to Damingfu. His treasured sword, unfortunately, was confiscated.

9. Chao Gai and the Gift Convoy

As Yang Zhi went into exile to Damingfu, he was sent on a mission to Dongjing thanks to his outstanding martial arts skills by Grand Secretary Liang, magistrate of Damingfu. His mission was to deliver a load of birthday gifts to Cai Jing, Liang's father-in-law.

Liang and Cai were both notorious corrupt officials. Seven people in Yuncheng County—Chao Gai, Wu Yong, Gongsun Sheng, Liu Tang, Ruan Xiao'er, Ruan Xiaowu and Ruan Xiaoqi got the message and conspired to rob the convoy so as to seek revenge for the exploited people.

Yang Zhi set out on the mission with some soldiers. One day, it was extremely hot. The soldiers were so tired that they left all the stuff on the roadside and went to rest under some trees.

At that moment, they saw a farmer liquor-vendor approaching them. The soldiers wanted to buy some liquor, but was stopped by Yang Zhi. He said, "Don't buy it. What if his liquor contains some type of knockout drug?"

The farmer said angrily, "Actually, I don't want to sell my liquor to you. Stop talking nonsense!"

After a while, there came seven jujube vendors who were pushing one-wheeled barrows along. Seeing that there was someone selling liquor, they rushed over, "We want a barrel of liquor."

The farmer pointed at Yang Zhi and said, "He said there's knockout drug in my liquor. I won't sell it to anyone!"

One of the jujube vendors replied, "That's his nonsense, not ours!"

The farmer said, "Fine, I'll sell one barrel to you."

After finishing one barrel of liquor, the seven jujube vendors wanted more. When the farmer looked away, one of them opened another barrel of liquor and began drinking with a bowl. The farmer took the bowl back and poured the liquor into the barrel again as soon as he noticed.

The soldiers' yearning for a drink now grew much stronger. They pleaded to Yang Zhi, "Shall we buy one barrel, too?"

Yang Zhi was also very thirsty. He thought, "The jujube vendors have finished drinking one barrel, and they've also drunk from the other barrel. This shows that there's no drugs in the liquor." So he accepted the soldiers' request and bought one barrel of liquor. The farmer left upon receiving the money.

It didn't take Yang Zhi and his soldiers very long to finish the whole barrel of liquor. A moment later, Yang Zhi started feeling dizzy. The seven jujube vendors said while laughing, "He's about to faint!"

Yang Zhi was startled to hear this. He struggled to stand up, but was too weak to do so. He tried to call the soldiers, only to find that all of them had already collapsed to the ground.

It turned out that the seven jujube vendors were none other than Chao Gai, Wu Yong, Gongsun Sheng, Liu Tang, Ruan Xiao'er, Ruan Xiaowu and Ruan Xiaoqi, and the farmer liquor-vendor was Bai Sheng. Liu Tang put the knockout drug into the second barrel after he drank some from it.

Chao Gai and his fellows poured out the jujubes onto the ground, and then loaded the wheelbarrows with all the birthday gifts. Then, they left joyfully.

10. Lu Zhishen and Yang Zhi Seizing Erlong Mountain

After losing all of the birthday gifts for Cai Jing, Yang Zhi was afraid that Grand Secretary Liang might vent his anger on him. He was too scared to return to Damingfu, so he decided to head for Liangshan and become an outlaw.

On his way to Liangshan, Yang Zhi ran into Cao Zheng, a good friend of his.

After learning about Yang Zhi's plan, Cao Zheng said, "A gang of bandits resides in Erlong Mountain nearby. Their ringleader is called Deng Long. You may as well go there and become the master by driving him away."

Yang Zhi replied, "That's a fantastic idea!"

Yang Zhi set off for Erlong Mountain the next morning. Just as he reached a forest, he saw a sturdy monk resting under a big tree.

Seeing Yang Zhi, the monk asked in a rude tone, "I am Lu

Zhishen, who are you?"

Yang Zhi was happily surprised, "So, you are the legendary Lu Zhishen! Aren't you at Xiangguo Temple?"

Lu Zhishen answered, "Since I saved Lin Chong's life in the Wild Boar Woods, Grand Marshal Gao had a deep hatred for me. He had sent many people to hunt me, so I had no other choice but to leave Xiangguo Temple."

Yang Zhi also told Lu Zhishen about his experience. The two soon became good friends since they regarded each other as heroes. They decided to go to Erlong Mountain together.

The next day, Cao Zheng brought a few men to assist Yang Zhi. They came up with a plan: They asked Lu Zhishen to take off his clothes and tied him up with a rope. After that, they headed for Erlong Mountain.

Upon their arrival, several men showed up. They asked Cao Zheng why he was there.

Cao Zheng answered, "This monk said he wanted to kill Boss Deng Long and become the master of Erlong Mountain himself. I tied him up when he was drunk. I came here to hand him over to Boss Deng." The men then led Cao Zheng and his fellows to meet Deng Long.

Deng became furious at the sight of Lu Zhishen. He cursed, "You damn monk! How dare you try to kill me?"

All of a sudden, Lu Zhishen broke away from the ropes and attacked Deng Long with his monk staff. Before Deng realized what had happened, he was killed.

Cao Zheng shouted to the others, "Follow our orders if you want to stay alive." Seeing that their ringleader had died, the bandits on Erlong Mountain all gave up their arms.

Since then, Yang Zhi and Lu Zhishen became the masters of Erlong Mountain.

11. Zhu Tong and Chao Gai

Upon returning to Damingfu, those who escorted the birthday gift convoy with Yang Zhi cheated Grand Secretary Liang by saying, "Yang Zhi tricked us with the bandits and robbed the convoy."

Liang told this to Cai Jing, his father-in-law. Cai got so furious that he ordered the magistrate of Jizhou for the immediate arrest of Yang Zhi as well as the other robbers.

Upon receiving Cai Jing's order, the magistrate wasted no time in dispatching He Tao to capture the bandits. However, after several months of hunting, He Tao still couldn't figure out who the robbers were. He became extremely anxious.

He Qing, his younger brother, told him, "A few days ago, I met Chao Gai, Bai Sheng and several others in Anle Village. They were carrying heavy trunks with them. Several days later, I heard that the birthday gift convoy was robbed. Chao Gai and his fellows must be the robbers!"

He Tao arrested Bai Sheng right away. Bai was terrified and begged, "Please don't kill me! I'll tell you everything! It was Chao Gai, Wu Yong and their confederates who robbed the birthday gift convoy!"

Chao Gai lived in Yuncheng County. On his way to capture Chao Gai, He Tao ran into Song Jiang, a minor official at the local government office. Learning that He Tao was hunting for Chao Gai, his good friend, Song Jiang secretly went to Chao Gai's residence and informed him about the situation, asking Chao Gai to flee right away.

He Tao informed the magistrate of Yuncheng County about the hunt. The magistrate immediately dispatched Zhu Tong and Lei Heng to capture Chao Gai.

The two arrived at Chao Gai's home before Chao managed to flee. As an acquaintance of Chao Gai, Zhu Tong didn't want to arrest him. So, he asked Lei Heng to lead several guards to the front gate while waiting for Chao Gai himself at the back door.

Chao Gai soon turned up at the back door. Seeing that there was no others around, Zhu Tong told Chao Gai to flee to Liangshan right away.

Chao Gai thanked him and began fleeing to Liangshan.

Chao Gai, Wu Yong and their companions were in the vicinity of Liangshan when they met three brothers, Ruan Xiao'er, Ruan Xiaowu and Ruan Xiaoqi, who wished to join Liangshan along with Chao Gai.

Chao Gai, Wu Yong and their fellows took the three brothers to Zhu Gui's pub. As a member of Liangshan, Zhu had already learned that Chao Gai and his pals robbed the birthday gifts, and thus regarded them as heroes. So he led them to Liangshan.

12. The Death of Wang Lun

When Chao Gai and his friends arrived, Wang Lun, the head of Liangshan, treated them to a feast.

During the feast, Chao Gai recounted their experience of robbing the birthday gift convoy. Everyone expressed their admiration for Chao Gai, Wu Yong and their companions. Wang Lun was the only one who didn't make any comments.

Chao Gai asked Wang, "What can we do for you, Boss Wang?"

Wang Lun didn't reply. He asked them to settle down first and he would talk about future arrangements in a few days.

The quick-witted Wu Yong figured out the reason right away: Wang Lun is jealous of our capabilities, so it's unlikely for him to allow us to stay here at Liangshan.

He then said to Chao Gai, "Wang Lun doesn't want to accommodate us at all. I sensed that Lin Chong is not happy with him. I'll find a way to have Lin Chong kill Wang Lun."

Wu Yong met Lin Chong the next morning and found out that he truly hated Wang Lun. While exhorting Lin Chong to stay calm, Wu Yong also used words to incite his fury.

Another day had passed. Wang Lun invited Chao Gai, Wu Yong and his fellows to his own house. Wang Lun presented a handsome amount of money to Chao Gai and said, "It's my pleasure to meet you. Unfortunately, Liangshan is too small for you guys to stay. Please accept the money and look for somewhere else."

Despite Chao Gai's repeated plea, Wang Lun still said no.

Lin Chong asked Wang Lun in a fury, "Why don't you let Brother Chao Gai and his friends stay at Liangshan?"

Wang Lun said to him, "Are you drunk? How dare you speak to me like that?"

Lin Chong said, "You're good for nothing, how could you be the leader?"

Wu Yong pretended to be exhorting him, "Please don't get angry. It's our fault. We shall leave right away!"

Lin Chong didn't listen to that at all. He seized Wang Lun and pointed his sword on Wang's nose, "What's the point of keeping you alive?" With these words, Lin Chong killed Wang Lun.

All the other bandits at Liangshan were frightened at seeing this and knelt down.

Wu Yong invited Lin Chong to be their new leader, but Lin Chong replied, "I recommend Brother Chao Gai to be our new leader."

In the end, Chao Gai became the new head of Liangshan, with Wu Yong ranking the second, Gongsun Sheng ranking the third, and Lin Chong ranking the fourth.

13. Song Jiang and Yan Poxi

Song Jiang served as a minor official in Yuncheng County. Chao Gai felt grateful to Song Jiang for having saved his life and so sent Liu Tang to look for him.

Liu Tang found Song Jiang and said, "Brother Chao Gai misses you very much. He asked me to give you 100 taels of gold, as well as this letter from him."

Song Jiang took the letter and one gold bar. He returned the rest of the gold to Liu Tang and said, "Liangshan is in urgent need of money now, so you'd better take it back. I shall take this gold bar as a token. Please thank Brother Chao Gai for me."

After delivering the letter, Liu Tang headed back to Liangshan. Song Jiang also returned home.

Song Jiang had a beautiful, young concubine named Yan Poxi. Since Song Jiang was always busy at work and seldom returned home, Yan secretly fell in love with another man. When Song Jiang got home, she was unhappy to see him.

The next morning, Song Jiang went to work again. When Yan Poxi woke up, she found a letter beside the bed. She read it and found the letter was from Chao Gai, the ringleader of Liangshan. She was overjoyed about this discovery. She planned to threaten Song Jiang with the letter, so that she could get the 100 taels of gold from him.

Song Jiang then noticed the letter was missing. He returned home in a hurry to look for it, but to no avail.

He thought, "It must be Yan Poxi who took my letter." Thus he asked Yan for it.

Yan Poxi told him, "Promise me two things if you want your letter back."

Song Jiang replied, "Okay, I'll do whatever you ask."

Yan Poxi then said, "First, this is my house from now on. You're not allowed in anymore. Second, give me the 100 taels of gold you got from Chao Gai."

Song Jiang explained, "I only took one gold bar and didn't keep the rest of the gold."

However hard Song Jiang tried to clarify, Yan didn't believe him. As a last resort, Song Jiang had to seize the letter by force. Just then, the knife he usually kept inside his clothes for self protection fell out while he was trying to grab the letter.

Yan Poxi yelled, "Help, help! Song Jiang is killing me!"

Out of anger and fear, Song Jiang picked up the knife and killed her. He also burned Chao Gai's letter immediately.

Song Jiang was worried that the murder might be discovered by the local government, so he quickly packed up and fled Yuncheng County.

14. Wu Song and the Tiger of Jingyang Ridge

There was a sturdy man named Wu Song who was gifted in martial arts.

At one noon, he was approaching Jingyang Ridge and entered a pub for lunch. A banner was seen over its gate that said "After three bowls of liquor, you would be too drunk to pass the ridge".

Wu Song took a seat and put his weapon—a wooden cudgel— aside. The pub owner served Wu Song three bowls of liquor. He drank it all at once and said, "Great liquor, one more please."

However, the owner wouldn't serve him anymore, saying, "I can't sell you any more liquor, sir. Haven't you seen the warning on our banner?"

"What does it mean?" Wu Song asked.

The pub owner answered, "Our liquor is so strong that all guests will be drunk after only three bowls. You wouldn't be able to make your way to Jingyang Ridge."

Wu Song replied, "That's nonsense, give me more!" The owner had to serve him more liquor.

One bowl after the other, Wu Song had 18 bowls of liquor in one breath. He laughed out loud, "Aha, stop saying no more than three bowls, I'm still fine after drinking 18 bowls!" Paying the bill, he took his wooden cudgel and left.

Seeing that Wu Song was heading for Jingyang Ridge, the pub owner said to him anxiously, "There's a big tiger on Jingyang Ridge. Don't go there alone! It's too dangerous! "

Wu Song didn't believe there was a tiger on the ridge. However hard the owner tried to persuade him, he wouldn't listen. He headed for Jingyang Ridge on his own.

As he was walking, a huge tiger suddenly jumped out of the woods, pouncing on him.

Startled, Wu Song made a quick dodge before striking at the tiger with his cudgel. However, the cudgel missed the target but hit a big tree instead, broken into halves. At that juncture, the tiger pounced on him again. Grabbing its head, Wu Song kicked the tiger hard in the face and eyes. It was hurting so badly that the tiger couldn't help digging deep into the ground with its front paws while roaring in pain. Wu Song pressed the tiger's head into the pit and continued pouncing at its head. At last, the tiger was killed.

The locals were extremely delighted to learn that the tiger which had harmed many lives of the local people was dead.

Wu Song became an instant hero for slaying the tiger. He received a warm welcome wherever he went. The county magistrate even granted him a minor official post.

15. Wu Song Tricking Sun Erniang

Shortly after becoming an official, Wu Song was exiled to Mengzhou for killing his foes who had murdered his elder brother.

On their way to Mengzhou, Wu Song had dinner at a pub with the two guards who were escorting him. The three sat down and put their parcels on the table.

Soon, a waitress in her thirties walked towards them, serving them with two plates of beef, a big pitcher of liquor and some steamed buns. While putting the buns on the table, she grabbed the parcel with one hand to judge the amount of money inside.

Wu Song noticed what the woman had done and thought, "I've heard that there is a pub nearby where the owner tricks customers with knockout drugs in order to steal their money. That's where I am now! Let me teach you a lesson!"

So he said to the waitress, "Do you have any better liquor to offer? We'd like to have a try!"

The woman answered, "We do have better liquor, but it will easily get you drunk."

Wu Song said, "The more intoxicating it is, the better. Bring it out please!"

That woman replied, "Just a moment, I'll fetch it for you."

The waitress went back into the room with a smile and poured three bowls of liquor. She secretly put a packet of knockout drugs into the liquor before serving them to the table. The two guards finished their bowls at once. While the woman was looking away, Wu Song dumped the liquor on the floor but pretended he had drunk it. He said loudly, "Fantastic! This liquor is far better!"

The two guards lost consciousness after having the drugged liquor. Wu Song pretended that he had also fainted.

Then, the waitress came to the table and opened Wu Song's parcel to take the money away.

As she was just taking out the money, Wu Song threw her onto the floor, beat her up while scolding, "Don't you know who I am? How dare you rob me!"

At that moment, a man entered the pub and pleaded to Wu Song, "My name is Zhang Qing, and she is my wife, Sun Erniang. We will no longer rob our customers. Please forgive us!"

Wu Song then spared the couple. Later on, Zhang Qing and Sun Erniang became Wu Song's good friends.

16. Wu Song Beating Door God Jiang

Upon his arrival at the government office in Mengzhou, Wu Song was put into a prison cell.

For several days, Shi En, son of the prison head, asked someone to send Wu Song food as well as daily necessities. However, he didn't reveal his own identity. Wu Song felt quite strange.

One day, someone came again at noon with liquor and dishes. Wu Song wouldn't let the man go unless he could invite his master to come over, or else he would go on a hunger strike.

The man had no choice but to look for Shi En.

After a while, Shi En came to Wu Song's ward and said to him, "I would like to ask you for a favor, but I'm worried that you are too tired after the long journey. So I just want you to have a few days of rest."

Wu Song replied, "Last year I even beat a tiger to death on the Jingyang Ridge when I was ailing. Just tell me your trouble! "

Shi En then told Wu Song what happened to him.

It turned out that the inn he owned was recently seized by a man nicknamed Door God Jiang, who also beat him up. Shi En wanted Wu Song to help him take the inn back.

Upon hearing this, Wu Song burst into laughter, "I hate those who seize other's things by force. Let's go find him!"

Wu Song found Door God Jiang with little effort. Jiang was aware that Wu Song was sent by Shi En, so the minute he saw Wu Song, he pounced on Wu Song to kill him.

However, he was kicked down immediately with his head being pressed against the ground by Wu Song. He was beaten up so badly that he kept begging loudly, "Please don't kill me!"

Wu Song stomped on Jiang's head and said, "Promise me three things and I'll let you go."

Jiang replied, "I'll accept 300 things if you wish!"

Wu Song said, "First, return the inn to Shi En right away; second, make an apology to him; third, leave Mengzhou as soon as possible. Or else I'll beat you up every time I see you."

Jiang said, "Alright, I promise!"

When hearing Jiang's promise, Wu Song set him free and told him, "I could even beat a tiger to death, let alone you."

Only then did Jiang realize he was beaten by none other than Wu Song, the tiger-killing hero.

Since then, Shi En reclaimed the inn. However, Jiang began to bear a deep hatred toward Wu Song. He was always thinking about taking revenge.

17. Inspector Zhang Framing Wu Song

Door God Jiang held a deep hatred toward Wu Song after he was beaten up, and as such, he had been biding his time to frame Wu Song.

One day, Inspector Zhang, a high-ranking official in Mengzhou, said to Wu Song, "I'd like to have you as my guard in my residence."

Wu Song accepted the offer since he thought it was a nice job. From then on, he followed Zhang everywhere as his guard. Zhang treated him very well and was even considering marrying one of the servant girls to him. Wu Song was truly grateful.

One evening, Wu Song suddenly heard a shout, "Catch the thief!"

Then he rushed over and asked, "Where's the thief?"

The girl who was to marry him said, "The thief has fled to the garden."

So Wu Song rushed to the garden. At that moment, seven or eight guards charged into the garden and tied him up. Then a few guards were sent to search his room, where a trunk was discovered under the bed. In the trunk, they found a lot of treasures that belonged to the Zhang family. Wu Song didn't know how to explain, so he chose to remain silent.

The next day, Zhang asked the guards to escort Wu Song to the government office. Learning that he was arrested, Shi En brought some money to the prison head immediately.

The prison head told Shi En, "This is nothing but a plot by Inspector Zhang and Instructor Zhang. They set Wu Song up. Door God Jiang is now hiding in Instructor Zhang's residence."

In order to save Wu Song, Shi En went to many people for help and paid the prefect a lot of money. Thanks to his efforts, Wu Song wasn't sentenced to death; instead, he was to be banished to Enzhou.

Two guards were dispatched to escort Wu Song. Shi En found him during the trip and sent him a secret message, saying, "The two guards escorting you want to end your life on the route. Watch out for them!"With that, Shi left.

As the three continued their journey to Enzhou, they were joined by two men each with a knife. At one time, the four exchanged a secret signal with each other plotting to kill Wu Song, but was detected by Wu.

While they were crossing a bridge over a big river, Wu Song suddenly turned around and kicked two guards into the river. The other two men wanted to flee from the bridge but were caught up by Wu Song. He killed one of them and seized the other to ask who was the instigator.

The man answered,"Door God Jiang sent us. He and Instructor Zhang ordered us to kill you on the way."

Wu Song asked, "Where is Jiang now?"

The man said,"He and Instructor Zhang are drinking at the

Lovebirds Tower in Inspector Zhang's residence."

Hearing that, Wu Song flew into a rage and killed him right away. He then headed for the Lovebirds Tower to seek revenge.

18. Wu Song's Retaliation

Having killed the four people who were sent to take his life, Wu Song headed back to Mengzhou to seek revenge against Inspector Zhang, Instructor Zhang and Door God Jiang.

The three were having a drink in a room at the Lovebirds Tower. Wu Song snuck into the tower, only to hear Jiang talking in the room, "Thank you very much, Your Honor, for helping us finish off Wu Song."

Inspector Zhang replied, "If it wasn't for Instructor Zhang's request, I wouldn't have interfered with this!" Then the three toasted the killing of Wu Song.

Hearing their conversation, Wu Song became furious and kicked the door open. The three were so frightened to see him that they all dropped their cups. Before Jiang could make a move, he was struck by Wu Song's sword and fell to the floor.

Just as Inspector Zhang was about to escape, Wu Song took the sword and hacked at his head. Zhang's head was instantly cut off.

Then Instructor Zhang held up a chair and flung it at Wu Song. The chair was caught by Wu Song and thrown back at Zhang. He was knocked down. Wu Song walked over and hacked him to death.

Looking at the three bodies, Wu Song said, "I'm the hero who killed the man-eating tiger, yet you set me up. Today I've done a good thing killing all of you!"

At a second thought, though, he realized that it would be a disaster if someone else was wrongly arrested for these murders. So he wrote several characters on the wall with the dead men's blood, which read "The murders were committed by Wu Song, the tiger-fighter".

Then he fled Mengzhou with his sword while it was dark.

19. Hua Rong at the Qingfeng Stronghold

After killing Yan Poxi, Song Jiang left Yuncheng County to look for Hua Rong, his old friend. Hua Rong was the head of the Qingfeng Stronghold who excelled in archery.

On his way to Qingfeng Stronghold, Song Jiang passed Qingfeng Mountain where resided a group of bandits. They admired Song Jiang so much that they invited him to stay for a few days. Song Jiang agreed.

One day, the bandits seized a woman who happened to be the wife of Liu Gao, another chief of the Qingfeng Stronghold.

Song Jiang then said to them, "I'm heading for the Qingfeng Stronghold, please set her free for my sake."

Out of reverence for Song Jiang, the bandits let the woman go.

Several days later, Song Jiang arrived at the Qingfeng Stronghold where he was led around by someone entrusted by Hua Rong.

As he was walking, Song Jiang encountered Liu Gao and his wife. Upon seeing Song, the woman pointed at him and told her husband, "That man is a bandit from Qingfeng Mountain."

Liu Gao then sent some people to capture Song Jiang. He planned to deliver him to the government office the next day.

The person entrusted by Hua Rong saw what happened and rushed back to report. Hua Rong wasted no time in leading dozens of soldiers to Liu Gao's residence to rescue Song Jiang.

Liu Gao was irritated. He ordered two men with great martial arts skills to lead hundreds of soldiers to Hua Rong's residence, attempting to retake Song Jiang.

Hua Rong told them, "This is something between me and Liu Gao. It has nothing to do with you. Now let me show you my shooting skills: first, I will shoot at the weapon held by the Door God on the left." Saying so, he shot one arrow and it hit the weapon precisely.

He went on, "Now I'll shoot at the hat of the Door God on the right." Saying so, he shot another arrow which also hit the target.

Hua Rong then added, "Can you see the man in white standing among you? I will shoot him in the heart." Hearing this, the man in white immediately ran away. So did all the other soldiers.

Hua Rong was worried that Liu Gao might send more people to capture Song Jiang, so he decided to leave Qingfeng Stronghold and head for Qingfeng Mountain along with Song.

20. Song Jiang's Drunk Poem

After staying with Song Jiang on Qingfeng Mountain for several days, Hua Rong tried to talk him into joining Liangshan. Song, however, didn't accept the request.

At that juncture, Song's father tricked him into returning home by asking Song Jiang's younger brother to write him a letter, saying that their father had passed away. Upon arriving at home,

Song Jiang was urged by his father to surrender himself to the authority. Song Jiang did as his father told him and was then sent into exile to Jiangzhou.

One day after Song arrived in Jiangzhou, he went to a famous restaurant Xunyanglou. He took a seat and started drinking.

Indulging himself in liquor for a while, Song Jiang became a little drunk. He asked the waiter for a brush and began writing a poem on the wall while drinking. The poem read "My heart is in Shandong, but I'm in Wu, I wander around alone sighing. If one day I realize my noble ambitions, who would dare laugh at me like they did to Huang Chao for not being a real man!" After finishing the poem, he added at the end: by Song Jiang from Yuncheng County.

Song Jiang kept drinking for a while and then left Xunyanglou for home. The next morning, he remembered nothing about what happened the day before.

There was a man named Huang Wenbing in Jiangzhou. When he came upon Song Jiang's poem on the wall at Xunyanglou one day, Huang was shocked. He considered it a poem with rebellious motives, so he reported his discovery to the prefect and showed him the poem he copied from the wall.

The prefect said, "A few days ago, I received a letter from my father who shared with me four popular sentences in Dongjing: '耗国因家木, 刀兵点水工. 纵横三十六, 拨乱在山东.' He urged me to take precautions here in Jiangzhou."

Huang Wenbing thought for a while and told the prefect, 耗国因家木 means the man who squanders state property must have 宀 and 木 in his name, indicating he has the surname 宋; 刀兵点水

工 means the one who holds military power has 水 and 工 in his given name, which is none other than the character 江. All these manifest that Song Jiang (宋江) is plotting a rebellion, which can also be proved by the poem he just wrote."

The prefect immediately dispatched guards to arrest Song Jiang. In spite of being warned in advance, Song Jiang still failed to flee. He was put into prison by the prefect.

21. Outlaws' Attempt to Save Song Jiang

Song Jiang was jailed by the prefect of Jiangzhou, who later sent Dai Zong to Dongjing to ask for instructions from Cai Jing about how to deal with Song's case.

As a good friend of Song Jiang, Dai Zong didn't go to Dongjing directly; instead, he made a stop at Liangshan first to consult with the outlaws hoping to find a way to rescue Song.

Wu Yong suggested saving Song Jiang on his way to Dongjing. Therefore, he forged a letter in Cai Jing's handwriting ordering the Jiangzhou prefect to send Song Jiang to Dongjing under escort.

Then Dai Zong gave the letter to the prefect. The handwriting in the forged letter had such a striking degree of resemblance to Cai's that the prefect didn't discern the forgery. Unfortunately, the astute Huang Wenbing discovered that the seal on it was a counterfeit. He immediately shared his discovery with the prefect, who was so furious that he also threw Dai Zong into jail and planned to put him to death together with Song Jiang.

Soon, the Liangshan outlaws received the news. They planned to go to Jiangzhou to rescue the two.

On the day of execution, the prefect dispatched many guards to escort Song Jiang and Dai Zong to the execution ground. They were scheduled to be executed at noon.

Many local people from Jiangzhou went to the execution ground. A few men who were holding snakes and swords also joined the crowd. Despite the guards' attempt to drive them away, the crowd was reluctant to leave.

It was noon. The prefect ordered two headsmen to execute Song Jiang and Dai Zong.

Out of the blue, one of the onlookers who was holding a snake suddenly threw it onto the ground. The crowd was so scared that the execution ground went into total chaos. At that moment, a dark-skinned sturdy man jumped out who was none other than Li Kui. He held up his axes and hacked the headsmen to death.

Two of the men holding swords came to Song Jiang and Dai Zong, carried them on their back and started to flee. The rest of their companions offered them protection while escaping from the execution ground.

In fact, those men carrying snakes and swords were all sent by Chao Gai, chief of the Liangshan outlaws. Having been saved by the outlaws, Song Jiang and Dai Zong settled down in Liangshan.

22. The Real and Fake Li Kui

Li Kui missed his mother very much. He planned to return home and bring her to Liangshan to start a new life there.

On his way back home, Li Kui was passing through some woods.

Suddenly, a man jumped out with an ax in each hand. He shouted at Li Kui, "Do you know who I am? I'm none other than Li Kui! Aren't you scared? I can spare your life as long as you give me all of your money!"

Li Kui burst into laughter on hearing that, and said, "I am Li Kui. Watch your ugly appearance before trying to impersonate me and rob passers-by!" Then he charged at the man with his sword.

The fake Li Kui was terrified, "Please forgive me! My real name is Li Gui; I live nearby. My mother is in her eighties and I rob people in the woods to provide for her. You are such a big name that people all revere you, that's why I impersonated you."

Li Kui was somewhat touched by Li Gui's words. He thought, "Li Gui also has a mother to provide for just like I do. I can't kill such a filial son!"

Li Kui let Li Gui off and gave him some money to start his own business, so he could earn more to take better care of his mother.

Li Gui accepted the money. He was very grateful to Li Kui, "Thank you for sparing my life! I promise I will neither impersonate you nor rob others." Saying that, Li Gui left the woods.

Li Kui continued his journey home. He reached a house, feeling exhausted and hungry. When he saw a woman inside, he asked her to sell him some food.

The woman didn't dare refuse. She walked into the kitchen to find something for him to eat.

Then Li Kui heard someone talking to her in the kitchen, "What a terrible day I had! I ran into the real Li Kui. Thank goodness I came up with an idea quickly to fool him into thinking that I had a mother to provide for, or else I would have been killed! That idiot took my word right away. He let me off and even gave me a lot of money!" It turned out that the house belonged to Li Gui, and the woman was none other than his wife.

The woman urged her husband to lower his voice, "Shh! A sturdy guy with very dark complexion just came in. He is right outside the kitchen. Go check whether he is Li Kui."

Li Gui replied, "If it is him, we will add some knockout drugs to his rice to make him faint, kill him and take his money so that we can move to the city."

Hearing the couple's conversation, Li Kui flew into a fury and thought: "I gave him money and spared his life, but he's now planning to kill me!" He then broke into the kitchen, killing Li Gui with his sword in one hack.

Li Gui's wife snuck away when Li Kui was not looking at her.

Li Kui found himself some food in the kitchen and set the house on fire. He then continued his journey home.

23. Li Kui and the Man-eating Tigers

After returning home, Li Kui found his mother had become blind. He was heartbroken, "Dear Mom, I'm Li Kui. I'm back!"

Lying in bed, his mom was so delighted to hear her son's voice, "My son, you are finally back! I've been missing you so much that I've gone blind from too much weeping."

Hearing this, Li Kui felt even more heart-broken. He lied to his mother, "I've become an official. I'm here to bring you back to my residence."

His mom was very pleased to hear this, "That's great! Let's wait for your brother and we shall go together."

Just then, Li Da, Li Kui's elder brother returned. He was caught by surprise upon seeing Li Kui. He said angrily, "I thought you would never come back!"

Mom explained to Li Da, "Your younger brother has become an official; he's here to pick us up."

Li Da replied, "Mom, he's lying to you! Don't believe what he said! He is now wanted by the government for his killing." Saying so, he left home.

Li Kui thought, "Perhaps my brother went to look for someone to have me arrested. I'd better leave soon!"

Leaving some money at home, Li Kui carried his mother on his back and left for Liangshan.

That evening, Li Kui carried his mother to a mountain. He asked his mom to sit on a rock and went to search for some water himself. Li Kui returned later, only to find his mother missing and some blood on the ground.

In panic, Li Kui traced the bloodstains, which led him to a cave where two small tigers were seen eating a human leg.

Li Kui suddenly realized: "My mom was eaten by these tigers!" Detecting that the leg belonged to none other than his mom, Li Kui was filled with fury and sadness, he dashed to the two small tigers and killed them with his sword.

Just at this moment, two big tigers appeared at the mouth of the cave. Seeing that their cubs were slain by Li Kui, they two fiercely sprang at him. Li Kui wasn't scared at all; he hacked one of the tigers in the neck, chopped off its head, and hacked the other in the stomach. It gave a painful roar and escaped out of the cave. Before long, the tiger tumbled to the ground and died.

Having killed the four tigers, Li Kui buried his mother in tears. He then knelt down in front of the grave, weeping for a long time before he reluctantly left the place.

24. Li Kui and the Zhu Brothers

After burying his mother, Li Kui left the mountain and arrived at a small town.

In the town, he encountered the wife of Li Gui. Upon seeing Li Kui, the woman immediately reported him to Squire Cao, a rich landlord. Hearing her words, Cao was overjoyed and thought, "If I capture Li Kui, the government will reward me with a lot of money!"

What could be done to arrest Li Kui given his unusual strength? Squire Cao came up with an idea: He invited Li Kui to a feast in his home, who became drunk while chatting joyfully with Cao.

Squire Cao asked someone to tie him up, and then sent Li Gui's wife to inform the authorities.

The government office dispatched several guards to the small town to arrest Li Kui.

When Li Kui left Liangshan, Song Jiang worried that he might cause some trouble. So he asked Zhu Gui to protect him secretly. Learning that Li Kui was captured, Zhu Gui became extremely worried but didn't know what he should do.

His younger brother Zhu Fu thought it over and said, "I have a plan to save Li Kui: Li Yun, the head of the escorting guards, was my master. So I can pretend to be congratulating him for the arrest of Li Kui, and then knock him out with drugs." Zhu Gui agreed to the plan.

Thus the Zhu brothers brought the drugged liquor along with some dishes and waited for Li Yun on the road.

After a while, Zhu Gui saw a group of people coming in their direction. Li Yun was in the front escorting Li Kui, Squire Cao and Li Gui's wife were also with them. The two seemed quite happy as they thought the government would reward them handsomely for capturing Li Kui.

Zhu Fu then presented a bowl of liquor to Li Yun, "Dear Master, congratulations on your arrest of Li Kui!"

Li Yun was so delighted that he finished all of the liquor and dishes along with his fellows. After a short while, all of them started collapsing to the ground.

Li Yun shouted, "Oh no! We were tricked!" As he was about to escape, dizziness struck him and he fainted as well.

Zhu Gui and Zhu Fu cut off the rope to set Li Kui free. Then Li Kui picked up a sword from the ground and killed Li Gui's wife and Squire Cao.

Zhu Fu tried to persuade Li Yun to join Liangshan. Li accepted as he was afraid of being punished by the authorities. The four went to Liangshan together.

25. Song Jiang's Attacks Against Zhu's Family Town

Not far from Liangshan, there was a town with Zhu Chaofeng as its leader. It had been on bad terms with Liangshan. The people of Zhu's Family Town saw the Liangshan outlaws as their enemy and always wanted to wipe them out. As Shi Qian was captured by the town, Song Jiang was planning an attack to annihilate Zhu's Family Town. To his dismay, he found that outsiders would easily get lost in the town because of its complicated terrain. So he waited outside the town with his troops while sending Shi Xiu to inquire about the routes.

As Shi Xiu entered Zhu's Family Town, an old man said to him, "It seems you are not a native from here. Run for your life quickly since the town will be in danger!"

Shi Xiu pretended to be surprised and asked, "Where does the danger come from?"

The old man explained, "Our town is on bad terms with Liangshan. Song Jiang is going to assault us soon!"

Shi Xiu feigned fear and cried, "I don't want to die in this town! Please show me a way out so I can go home."

Feeling pity for Shi Xiu, the old man told him, "Make a turn every time you see a poplar tree. Bear in mind it's impossible to exit the town through roads without poplars."

Shi Xiu thanked the old man and was about to leave. Suddenly, a shout was heard, "Attention please! The Liangshan bandits will come to attack us tonight. We will use the red lanterns as signals; upon seeing it, everybody should charge at the enemies and capture them!"

Song Jiang became very anxious after waiting for Shi Xiu to come out of Zhu's Family Town for a long time. He hastily led his troops into the town to rescue Shi Xiu. Unfortunately, they soon lost their way. Just as Song Jiang was wondering which direction to go, people in the town began shooting arrows at them which killed many soldiers. Song said in a resigned tone, "I had never thought that we would be killed here at Zhu's Family Town."

At that juncture, they heard someone yelling, "Turn whenever you see a poplar, and we will get out of here for sure!" It turned out that Shi Xiu had arrived in time to rescue his companions.

As they were retreating, they found the number of Zhu soldiers kept increasing. Shi Xiu said, "They are using the red lantern as a signal, the person holding the lantern will follow whichever direction we go, so their soldiers are moving toward us."

Hua Rong said, "I have an idea." He then shot an arrow which put out the candle in the red lantern.

Without the lighted lantern as a signal, the Zhu soldiers didn't know which way to go. Seizing the chance, Song Jiang led his troops out of the town and safely returned to Liangshan.

26. Sister Gu's Raid on the Prison

There was a pub in Dengzhou run by Sun Xin and his wife, Sister Gu. The couple both had excellent martial arts skills. Gu had two cousins, Xie Zhen and Xie Bao, who were renowned hunters in the region.

One day, when the brothers spotted an injured tiger, they started chasing it right away. The tiger was bleeding while running. Eventually it got so exhausted that it tumbled down a hill. The tiger coincidentally fell into the garden of Squire Mao, so Xie Zhen and Xie Bao rushed to Mao's residence to search for it.

Squire Mao's son hid the tiger immediately after he saw the tiger falling into their garden.

The Xie brothers arrived at Mao's residence and demanded the return of the tiger. However, Squire Mao and his son refused to hand it over. They even tried to frame them by saying the two had broken into their house for robbery. As a result, Xie Zhen and Xie Bao were arrested and sent to the authorities.

Learning that her cousins were arrested, Sister Gu became very anxious. She quickly went to her husband Sun Xin, trying to figure out a way to rescue them.

Sun Xin said, "Since the Mao family was well connected with the government, the authorities will surely take their side. The only way for us to rescue the Xie brothers will be breaking into the jail. But given there are so many prison guards there, it's a mission impossible for only two of us. I will turn to my brother for help."

Sun Xin's elder brother was called Sun Li, who was a minor officer in Dengzhou. Having been told by Sun Xin about the plan to rescue the Xie brothers, Sun Li was not willing to offer his help.

Sister Gu was irritated and said to Sun Li, "You can choose not to go, but we will go for sure. We will flee to Liangshan after rescuing them, and you will be hunted by the authorities once we are gone. Just stay here and wait for your arrest!"

Feeling that Gu had a point, Sun Li had to agree to extend a helping hand.

The next evening, Sister Gu entered the prison cell by pretending to send food to the Xie brothers. She collaborated with Sun Li and Sun Xin who were waiting outside and succeeded in rescuing the Xie brothers out of the jail.

Having left the jail, Sun Li and his companions went to the Mao residence and killed Squire Mao and his son. Then they left for Liangshan.

27. Song Jiang Capturing Zhu's Family Town

When the Xie brothers, Sun Li, Sun Xin and Sister Gu arrived at Liangshan, Song Jiang was planning the third attack against Zhu's Family Town.

Since Song's two previous attempts of capturing the town both failed, Sun Li offered a suggestion. "The martial arts instructor of Zhu's Family Town is a close friend of mine. I can go there to seek his help while collecting some information about the enemies in order to help you defeat them."

Song Jiang was very pleased to hear that. He accepted Sun Li's idea.

The next day, Sun Li led Sun Xin and Sister Gu to Zhu's Family Town. All three disguised themselves as government officers.

Upon seeing Sun Li, the martial arts instructor was glad and asked, "I thought you are in Dengzhou, what has brought you here?"

Sun Li replied, "The magistrate of Dengzhou dispatched me to Yuncheng County to deal with bandits. I was passing through the town so I thought I'd better drop in on you."

Two days later, Song Jiang gathered his troops and launched

another assault on Zhu's Family Town. He asked Sun Li to make a false arrest of Shi Xiu, in order to gain the trust of Zhu Chaofeng. As expected, Zhu started to trust Sun since Sun had caught a Liangshan bandit.

During the past few days, Sun Li had obtained enough information about Zhu's Family Town. He then found a chance to meet Shi Xiu, telling him to get ready for further actions.

Another day had passed. The three sons of Zhu Chaofeng took most of the Zhu soldiers with them to fight against Song Jiang while leaving their father and Sun Li behind to protect their home. Only very few people were left behind as a defense for the town.

When Zhu Chaofeng was not paying attention, Sun Li hung the Liangshan flag over the entrance of Zhu's Family Town. Upon seeing the flag, the Liangshan soldiers dashed into the town. Sun Xin and Sister Gu then went to the prison and rescued Shi Xiu.

Seeing this dangerous situation, Zhu Chaofeng planned to escape. Shi Xiu discovered that and killed Zhu with his sword. Subsequently, Zhu's three sons were killed by Li Kui and his companions.

After capturing the town, Song Jiang and his soldiers returned to Liangshan.

28. Lei Heng and Bai Xiuying

In Yuncheng County, there was a minor official named Lei Heng who loved Chinese opera.

One day, he went to the theater to watch an opera. An actress by the name of Bai Xiuying was performing on stage. She sang so well that the audience gave her many rounds of warm applause.

After the play was over, Bai took out a plate and said to the audience, "If you like my performance, please grant me a reward."

As Lei Heng was sitting in the very front, Bai Xiuying came to him first.

Lei Heng tried to look for some money in his pocket, but didn't find any. He had to explain to Bai and promised her a reward the next day.

Bai Xiuying didn't believe he had brought no money with him. She thought he was just too mean. So, she started a quarrel with him.

At that moment, Bai's father came over and ridiculed Lei Heng as a stingy person.

Lei Heng couldn't control his temper any longer and tried to hit Bai's father. Seeing that Lei Heng was hitting someone, some audience came over and persuaded him to return home.

Since Bai Xiuying was the mistress of the county magistrate, nobody had ever dared offend her. Seeing that her father was beaten by Lei Heng, the woman reported the situation to the magistrate while weeping.

Upon hearing that, the magistrate was furious. He ordered his soldiers to arrest Lei Heng. Lei was then tied up at the theater entrance. A wooden yoke with his offenses written on it was placed around his neck.

When Lei Heng's mother learned of this situation, she rushed to the theater entrance, only to find her son with bruises all over his body. Seeing this, she was heartbroken. She cursed while crying, "Bai Xiuying is such a wicked woman to bully my son like this!"

Hearing what Lei's mother said, Bai Xiuying became furious and dashed out of the theater. She gave Lei's mother several slaps in the face, and the old lady almost tumbled down.

Lei Heng was a filial son. Seeing that his mother was hurt, he broke the rope binding him and held up the yoke to strike Bai Xiuying's head. Bai was killed instantly.

The county magistrate flew into a fury upon learning of the death of his mistress. He then dispatched Zhu Tong to escort Lei Heng to Jizhou, where Lei would be killed.

Zhu Tong and Lei Heng were close friends. When they reached a forest, Zhu Tong secretly told Lei Heng, "Go home to pick up your mom and leave Yuncheng as quickly as possible!"

Lei Heng thanked Zhu Tong and fled for Liangshan along with his mother.

29. Zhu Tong Seeking Shelter

Zhu Tong was banished to Cangzhou by the county magistrate as a punishment for his release of Lei Heng. The prefect of Cangzhou asked Zhu Tong to take care of his little son.

One evening, Zhu Tong was playing with the boy on the street. Suddenly, he felt someone was pulling him. He turned around. To his surprise, he saw Lei Heng and Wu Yong.

Zhu Tong told the boy, "I will buy some candy for you. Wait here for me and don't go anywhere, okay?"

He then took Lei Heng and Wu Yong to a quiet place and asked Lei, "Why are you here?"

Lei Heng answered, "You saved my life. Brother Song Jiang is very grateful for what you've done for me. So he sent me and Brother Wu here to invite you to Liangshan."

Zhu Tong declined the offer, "The prefect is very kind to me. I don't want to go anywhere for now. I just want to lead a peaceful life as an ordinary person."

Seeing that Zhu Tong was very firm with his decision, Wu Yong said, "Since you are not willing to go with us, we won't keep trying to persuade you."

Zhu Tong rushed back to look for the child, but to no avail.

Lei Heng told him, "Don't worry, the boy might be with Li Kui. Let's go find them."

The three arrived at a forest where they encountered Li Kui.

Zhu Tong asked him anxiously, "Where's the boy?"

Li Kui answered, "He's sleeping in the woods. Go and look for yourself."

Zhu Tong ran into the woods, but found the child was dead on the ground.

In a fury, Zhu Tong dashed out of the forest. He yelled at Li Kui, "Why did you kill an innocent child? You're so brutal!" Upon saying so, Zhu Tong sprang at Li Kui and tried to end his life.

Wu Yong immediately stopped him and said, "You will be killed by the prefect as soon as you return. You'd better go with us."

Zhu Tong thought, "I'll surely be killed if the prefect learns his son is dead. I'd better go with them."

Although Zhu Tong promised to join the outlaws, he refused to talk to Li Kui because Li killed the innocent child.

30. Stealing a Suit of Armor

There was a man named Xu Ning in Dongjing, who had excellent martial arts skills. Song Jiang was eager to invite him to Liangshan to be their martial arts instructor.

But what if Xu Ning was not willing to come?

It turned out that Tang Long, one of Xu's relatives, had already joined Liangshan. He told the other outlaws, "Xu Ning regards one of his suits of armor as his own life. If we could steal it, I might be able to persuade him to come here."

Song Jiang thus sent Shi Qian to steal the suit of armor from Xu's residence and asked Tang Long to assist him.

The suit of armor was placed inside a red box. At night, Shi Qian took the box away when Xu Ning didn't notice.

Xu was heartbroken upon finding his suit of armor stolen.

The next day, Tang Long came to Xu Ning and said to him, "Was your armor stolen? I just saw a man with a red box heading for Shandong."

Hearing that, Xu Ning immediately asked Tang Long to lead him and chase that person.

After chasing for two days, they sat under a tree for a rest in the evening.

Suddenly, Tang Long yelled, "Look! That guy is carrying a red box on his back!"

Xu Ning looked in the direction that Tang Long pointed toward, only to see Shi Qian was sitting beneath a tree with the red box on his back.

In a fury, Xu Ning dashed over and seized Shi Qian, "That's my armor! Give it back to me!"

Shi Qian replied immediately, "I sold it last night. If you let me go, I'll help you get it back."

Therefore, Xu Ning followed Shi Qian to look for his suit of armor. But it hadn't occurred to him that they were actually heading for Liangshan.

Just before their arrival, Shi Qian treated Xu Ning with a bowl of drugged liquor, which made him faint. The others soon carried him onto a carriage and they went on their journey again.

Upon arriving at Liangshan, Tang Long revealed the entire story to Xu Ning. It turned out that everything had been arranged by Tang Long. He had pretended to have led Xu to catch Shi Qian, which brought Xu Ning all the way to Shandong. At this point, Xu Ning was made faint by the drugged liquor and was carried to Liangshan.

Song Jiang returned the armor to Xu Ning, and invited him to stay on the mountain and pass on his martial arts skills to the outlaws.

Xu Ning had a deep admiration for the Liangshan outlaws, so he accepted Song Jiang's request and had since settled on the mountain to act as the martial arts instructor.

31. The Death of Chao Gai

As the foremost leader of Liangshan, Chao Gai enjoyed wide respect among the other outlaws. Unfortunately he had one outstanding shortcoming: he sometimes took reckless actions before careful thinking.

One day, someone came to Liangshan and said to him, "I had planned to present you with a fine horse to show my deep admiration for the Liangshan heroes. Regrettably, it was seized at Zeng's Family Fortress by Shi Wengong, teacher of the 'Five Tigers of the Zeng Family'."

Chao Gai became furious upon hearing that. Immediately, he led his troops and launched an attack against the Zeng's Family Fortress to reclaim the horse.

Chao Gai was stopped by Lin Chong just outside the fortress, as he was about to dash over and attack the five sons of Zeng Nong.

Lin Chong then took his weapon and began to fight the "Five Tigers". Being no match for Lin, the five sons fled back into the fortress with their soldiers.

Chao Gai and his troops waited outside the fortress for three days, but the five sons did not dare to come out again.

On the fourth day, two monks came to Chao Gai and told him, "We know where the 'Five Tigers' live and can lead you to capture them."

Chao Gai was overjoyed upon hearing that. But Lin Chong suspected the two monks were sent by the enemy to deceive Chao Gai.

Detecting Lin Chong's suspicion, the two monks said, "Monks never tell lies. We know that the Liangshan heroes are all kind-hearted people, so we are here on our own initiative to show you the way."

Thinking that the monks were telling the truth, Chao Gai said to Lin Chong, "I believe them. Tonight, I will lead some soldiers to catch the 'Five Tigers'. You can stay on the mountain to wait for my message."

In the evening, Chao Gai and his troops entered Zeng's Family Fortress following the two monks. After a while, they arrived at a secluded forest where the monks suddenly disappeared. Chao Gai then realized that he was cheated. He ordered an immediate retreat of the troops, but it was too late.

The "Five Tigers of the Zeng Family" and their soldiers besieged Chao Gai. Then Shi Wengong shot an arrow at Chao Gai which hit his head.

Lin Chong rescued Chao Gai and sent him back to Liangshan immediately. Unfortunately, his wound was incurable as the arrow that hit him was a poisoned one.

Right before his death, Chao Gai told Song Jiang, "Whoever catches Shi Wengong in the future shall become the new leader of Liangshan." With these words, he passed away.

32. Wu Yong Plays a Fortune Teller

There was a man in Daming Prefecture named Lu Junyi who possessed outstanding martial arts skills.

Song Jiang planned to ask Lu to be the commander-in-chief for another assault on Zeng's Family Fortress, so he dispatched Wu

Yong and Li Kui to Daming Prefecture in the hope of tricking him into joining Liangshan.

One day, Wu Yong disguised himself as a fortune teller and Li Kui posed as his servant. The two then arrived in Daming Prefecture.

Lu Junyi came upon Wu Yong on the street. Wu said to him, "I can predict one's future through fortune telling."

Lu Junyi then invited Wu Yong to his residence and asked him what the future held for him.

Wu Yong told him, "Your future is ominous since there is an imminent fatal danger."

Lu asked anxiously, "Can the danger be avoided?"

Wu Yong replied, "That's easy, sir. Your safety could be ensured as long as you leave Daming Prefecture and flee 1,000 *li* southeast."

Wu Yong went on, "Here, I have a poem that portrays your future. I will read it and you can write it on the wall so as to check if my prediction is right or not when the danger occurs."

The poem read:

"There is a small boat in the reeds,

You will soon pass by this place;

If you know the hidden reason and escape,

Your worries could come to an end."

Seeing that Lu had written the poem on the wall, Wu Yong left his residence with Li Kui for Liangshan.

Feeling puzzled, Li Kui asked Wu, "Only with a few words between you and Lu, you could make him come to Liangshan?"

Wu Yong answered, "Sure! I asked him to travel 1,000 *li* to the southeast, where he will pass by Liangshan. As soon as he gets there, we will be able to trick him into joining us. If you read the poem on the wall of his house, you can find the first character of each line forms the phrase 卢俊义反 (Lu Junyi is going to plot a rebellion), which constitutes a capital offense. As such, he would be sentenced to death by the authorities. By that time, he will have no other choice but to stay at Liangshan."

A few days later, Lu Junyi left Daming Prefecture and headed southeast. As he passed by Liangshan, Song Jiang extended him an invitation.

Lu found it difficult to refuse and had to stay at Liangshan for several days. However, he was thinking about leaving the place as he wasn't willing to become an outlaw.

33. Yan Qing and Lu Junyi

Since Lu Junyi wasn't willing to stay at Liangshan, Song Jiang had to let him go home.

Lu had a servant named Yan Qing, who was remarkably skillful at shooting.

Lu ran into Yan Qing on his way home. Yan Qing said to him in tears, "Master, soon after you left home, your wife and the steward went to the government office and framed you as a bandit. They got married and drove me out. You'd better return to Liangshan right now; if you go home, you will definitely be arrested by the authorities."

Lu didn't believe Yan Qing's words. Feeling heartbroken, Yan Qing left his master.

Lu's wife and the steward were caught unprepared by his return. They feigned a warm reception for Lu Junyi, but then secretly left home and informed the authorities about his return.

After a while, some guards arrived at Lu's residence and escorted him to the government office.

The steward told the magistrate, "Lu Junyi wrote a poem on his wall, the first character of each line forms the phrase 卢俊义反 (meaning "Lu Junyi is going to plot a rebellion"), which proves his evil intentions."

The magistrate sent people to check Lu's house, and they found the poem on the wall. He was convinced that Lu Junyi was indeed plotting a rebellion. As a result, Lu would be banished to Shamen Island.

Only then did Lu realize that Yan Qing was telling the truth that his wife and the steward were framing him.

Lu's wife and the steward were still worried that he might survive this catastrophe. So they found the two guards who were going to escort Lu Junyi to Shamen Island and gave them a lot of money, asking the two to kill Lu on the way.

Upon seeing the huge amount of money, the two guards accepted the steward's request right away.

On their way to the island, the two led Lu Junyi to a forest where they planned to kill him.

All of a sudden, two arrows were shot down from a tree and killed the two guards on the spot.

Then Yan Qing jumped off the tree, hugged his master and said to him in tears, "I've been following you to find a chance to rescue you. Seeing that the two guards were about to kill you, I had to end their lives."

Lu Junyi said, "Since we can never return to Daming Prefecture, where shall we go?"

Yan Qing replied, "The only shelter we can seek is Liangshan Marsh." Upon saying so, he carried his master on his back and headed for Liangshan.

34. Song Jiang Attacks Daming Prefecture

On their way to Liangshan, Lu Junyi was captured again by the government forces. Yan Qing had no choice but to head for Liangshan to seek help.

Song Jiang became extremely anxious upon learning the news.

Wu Yong said to him, "Don't worry, brother. We can seize this opportunity to launch an attack against Daming Prefecture and take their grain and food."

Song Jiang accepted Wu Yong's plan.

Wu Yong asked Shi Qian to first sneak into the prefecture and set fire during the evening of the Lantern Festival. Then he ordered Lin Chong, Xu Ning, Li Kui and Lei Heng to lead some soldiers and wait at the four main gates of the prefecture. Upon seeing the fire, they would simultaneously attack the four gates.

Shi Qian stole into Daming Prefecture on the evening of the Lantern Festival. He found a secluded place and started to set fire; the fire quickly grew and spread.

At that moment, someone yelled on the street, "Look! The Liangshan troops have besieged our prefecture and are going to attack us!" People in the prefecture were so scared that they all fled home.

Upon seeing the fire, Lin Chong and his companions who were waiting outside started their attack against the four main gates. The defending soldiers became extremely anxious and reported the situation to Grand Secretary Liang, magistrate of Daming Prefecture.

Liang was enjoying the full moon at his residence. Suddenly a shout was heard, "The Liangshan bandits are attacking us!"Terrified, the magistrate mounted his horse, trying to flee with some soldiers.

However, Liangshan troops could be seen at each of the four main gates. Liang had to look for a way out while trying his best to dodge their attack. Thanks to the protection offered by his soldiers, the magistrate finally made his way out of the prefecture.

Song Jiang and his troops soon captured Daming Prefecture. They broke into the prison and rescued Lu Junyi. The steward was later killed.

The outlaws divided the prefecture's grain storage into two portions; one portion was shared by the local people, and the rest was brought back to Liangshan.

35. Shi Wengong's Arrest

Chao Gai was shot and killed by Shi Wengong when he launched an assault against Zeng's Family Fortress. Subsequently, Shi sent troops twice and seized many horses from Liangshan.

Song Jiang couldn't bear the bullying any longer and decided to attack Zeng's Family Fortress.

Zeng Nong, the headman of Zeng's Family Fortress, sent his eldest son and his youngest son along with Shi Wengong to fight the Liangshan troops. However, the Liangshan outlaws were so mighty that both of his sons were killed.

Having lost two sons, Zeng Nong was heartbroken. Zeng was concerned about the lives of his other three sons, so he asked Shi Wengong to write a letter of reconciliation to Song Jiang.

When Song Jiang received the letter, he could only find phrases such as "we are ready to return the horses we have taken", but not one word of apology. So he became furious and said, "They killed Brother Chao Gai, but didn't offer a single word of apology!"

After Wu Yong read the letter, he whispered a few words to Song Jiang who in turn became very happy. Song Jiang immediately wrote back to Zeng Nong, pledging an end of confrontation; at the same time, he made a request to Zeng that besides returning the horses, they should also escort those robbers to Liangshan along with the horses.

The request was accepted by Zeng Nong and Shi Wengong, who later handed over both the horses and the robbers to Song Jiang.

Song Jiang called in one of the robbers and said to him, "I'd like to ask you for a favor. I will spare your life once it is done." The robber readily accepted his condition.

Song Jiang then asked him to pretend to flee back to Zeng's Family Fortress and tell Shi Wengong, "Song Jiang's mind is set on reclaiming the horses, so he doesn't care about anything else now. We will surely succeed if we launch a sudden attack against them tonight."

It turned out that Shi Wengong accepted the suggestion without even the slightest suspicion. He ordered all of his soldiers to get ready for an assault against Song Jiang's camp that evening.

In the evening, Shi Wengong charged into Song Jiang's camp with his troops; however, nobody was found there. Only then did he realize that he was deceived by Song Jiang. As Shi was about to escape, many Liangshan soldiers dashed out and killed Zeng's three sons. Shi Wengong's horse ran very fast and it carried him into the woods.

Lu Junyi and Yan Qing were waiting for Shi right there. Being no match for the two, Shi Wengong was captured.

36. A Great Gathering of Heroes

Song Jiang had Shi Wengong executed in front of Chao Gai's memorial tablet. He then summoned all the other outlaws and said to them, "We still remember that when Brother Chao Gai was passing away, he said, 'Whoever catches Shi Wengong shall become the leader of Liangshan.' Today, Lu Junyi did that, so we should make him our new leader."

Lu Junyi turned town the request right away, "No, that won't do. I'm not qualified to be the leader. I'm already gratified to be allowed to stay at Liangshan with all the heroes."

Song Jiang replied, "I don't mean to be modest, but the fact is that you are far more capable than me. So you deserve to be the leader of Liangshan."

Upon hearing that, Lu immediately knelt down and said, "Don't try to persuade me anymore, brother. I won't be the leader."

In fact, Wu Yong didn't consider Lu Junyi as a desirable leader because he was worried that Lu wasn't capable enough to manage the affairs of Liangshan. He then said to Song Jiang, "I recommend Brother Song to be our top leader, and Brother Lu to rank as the second. I'm afraid you would let us down if you continue with the resignation."

Li Kui couldn't control his emotions any longer. Upon listening to Wu Yong, he said to Song Jiang in a loud voice, "Everyone wants you to be our leader. If you refuse again, we'd better be dissolved."

The other outlaws echoed Li Kui and tried to persuade Song Jiang as well. At last, Song Jiang said, "I have an idea. There are two places that I want to conquer; one is Dongping Prefecture, the other is Dongchang Prefecture. Lu Junyi and I can each lead an army to attack one of the two places, whoever gains victory first shall become the new leader. "

Everyone agreed with his proposal. Song Jiang then led his troops to attack Dongping Prefecture, while Lu Junyi set out for Dongchang Prefecture.

It turned out that Song Jiang succeeded first and thus officially became the head of Liangshan.

On the day when Song Jiang was sworn in, all outlaws assembled at the Hall of Loyalty and Righteousness. They were seated according to their ranks at Liangshan. The total number of the heroes added up to be 108.

Song Jiang made a suggestion, "Today, I'm more than delighted to witness our 108 brothers gather together here at Liangshan. I would like to build a stone tablet with all our names on it. What do you think?"

Everybody thought that was a good idea.

Since then, Liangshan thrived. The outlaws went on robbing the evil-doers in order to help those in need, which won them wide popularity among the people.

词汇表
Vocabulary List

暗号	*n.*	ànhào	secret signal
拔	*v.*	bá	pull out
白杨树	*n.*	báiyángshù	white poplar
包围	*v.*	bāowéi	besiege, surround
宝刀	*n.*	bǎodāo	treasured sword
报仇	*v.*	bàochóu	take revenge
北	*n.*	běi	north
逼	*v.*	bī	force, compel
笔	*n.*	bǐ	brush, pen
才	*adv.*	cái	only when
菜地	*n.*	càidì	vegetable plot
残忍	*adj.*	cánrěn	brutal, ruthless
藏	*v.*	cáng	hide, conceal
唱	*v.*	chàng	sing
车	*n.*	chē	cart
冲动	*adj.*	chōngdòng	impetuous
仇	*n.*	chóu	hatred, enmity
仇人	*n.*	chóurén	foe
出战	*v.*	chūzhàn	go into battle
床	*n.*	chuáng	bed
闯祸	*v.*	chuǎnghuò	cause troubles
脆骨	*n.*	cuìgǔ	gristle
打败	*v.*	dǎbài	defeat
打开	*v.*	dǎkāi	open
打探	*v.*	dǎtàn	probe information about
带领	*v.*	dàilǐng	lead
当成	*v.*	dàngchéng	take for
得罪	*v.*	dézuì	offend, displease
地主	*n.*	dìzhǔ	landlord
第	*pref.*	dì	(marker of ordinal numerals)
店小二	*n.*	diànxiǎo'èr	waiter

动	v.	dòng	move
毒	n.	dú	poison
对付	v.	duìfu	deal with
耳光	n.	ěrguāng	slap in the face
饭	n.	fàn	dinner
房子	n.	fángzi	house
肥	adj.	féi	fat
粪坑	n.	fènkēng	manure pit
愤怒	adj.	fènnù	angry, furious
封	m.w.	fēng	(for sth. enveloped)
斧子	n.	fǔzi	ax
副	m.w.	fù	set
攻打	v.	gōngdǎ	attack, assault
咕噜噜	onom.	gūlūlū	rumble, roll
管	v.	guǎn	attend to, interfere
跪	v.	guì	kneel
河	n.	hé	river
花园	n.	huāyuán	garden
话	n.	huà	word, talk
监狱	n.	jiānyù	prison, jail
见	v.	jiàn	meet, see
箭	n.	jiàn	arrow
斤	m.w.	jīn	*jin*, a unit for measuring weight which equals 0.5 kg
进入	v.	jìnrù	enter
酒	n.	jiǔ	alcohol, liquor
酒馆	n.	jiǔguǎn	pub
句	m.w.	jù	sentence
聚	v.	jù	gather, assemble
军营	n.	jūnyíng	military camp
坑	n.	kēng	pit
捆	v.	kǔn	tie, bind
啦	part.	la	(fusion of 了 and 啊)
里面	n.	lǐmiàn	inside
里应外合		lǐyìng-wàihé	collaborate from within with forces from without

猎人	*n.*	lièrén	hunter
另	*pron.*	lìng	other
流	*v.*	liú	(of liquid) flow
柳树	*n.*	liǔshù	willow tree
摞	*v.*	luò	pile up
马车	*n.*	mǎchē	carriage
埋	*v.*	mái	bury
冒充	*v.*	màochōng	impersonate, pass…off as
没收	*v.*	mòshōu	confiscate
面	*m.w.*	miàn	(used for flags, mirrors, etc.)
面子	*n.*	miànzi	face, reputation
谋反	*v.*	móufǎn	conspire against the state
木棒	*n.*	mùbàng	wooden club
牛肉	*n.*	niúròu	beef
怒火	*n.*	nùhuǒ	fury
爬	*v.*	pá	climb, crawl
排行	*v.*	páiháng	be ranked as
盘	*m.w.*	pán	plate
判	*v.*	pàn	sentence, make a ruling
偏僻	*adj.*	piānpì	remote, secluded
扑	*v.*	pū	spring at
扑通	*onom.*	pūtōng	splash, flop
仆人	*n.*	púrén	servant
欺负	*v.*	qīfu	bully
旗子	*n.*	qízi	flag, banner
强盗	*n.*	qiángdào	bandit, robber
强壮	*adj.*	qiángzhuàng	strong, sturdy
强迫	*v.*	qiǎngpò	force, compel
求	*v.*	qiú	beg
饶	*v.*	ráo	forgive, spare
肉	*n.*	ròu	meat
肉馅	*n.*	ròuxiàn	minced meat stuffing
散伙	*v.*	sànhuǒ	dissolve, disband
山洞	*n.*	shāndòng	mountain cave
煽动	*v.*	shāndòng	incite

擅自	adv.	shànzì	presumptuously
赡养	v.	shànyǎng	provide for
伤	n.	shāng	injury, wound
烧	v.	shāo	burn
射	v.	shè	shoot
声	n.	shēng	sound, voice
尸体	n.	shītǐ	dead body
石碑	n.	shíbēi	stone tablet
手	n.	shǒu	hand
首领	n.	shǒulǐng	head, leader, chief
树林	n.	shùlín	woods, forest
死罪	n.	sǐzuì	capital offense
虽然	conj.	suīrán	although, though
贪官	n.	tānguān	corrupt official
探路	v.	tànlù	explore the way
讨好	v.	tǎohǎo	curry favor with
疼爱	v.	téng'ài	love dearly
踢	v.	tī	kick
天 [1]	n.	tiān	day
天 [2]	n.	tiān	sky
跳	v.	tiào	jump
桶	n.	tǒng	barrel
偷	v.	tōu	steal
偷偷	adv.	tōutōu	secretly
头	n.	tóu	head
挖	v.	wā	dig
外号	n.	wàihào	nickname
晚	adj.	wǎn	late
威胁	v.	wēixié	threaten
乌鸦	n.	wūyā	crow
武器	n.	wǔqì	weapon
戏院	n.	xìyuàn	theater
陷害	v.	xiànhài	frame up
箱子	n.	xiāngzi	trunk
消灭	v.	xiāomiè	wipe out, annihilate

信	*n.*	xìn	letter
丫鬟	*n.*	yāhuan	servant girl, maid
压	*v.*	yā	weigh down
押送	*v.*	yāsòng	escort
衙役	*n.*	yáyì	escorting guard
沿	*prep.*	yán	along
摇摇晃晃	*v.*	yáoyáohuànghuàng	stumble one's way
以后	*n.*	yǐhòu	later, afterwards
印章	*n.*	yìnzhāng	seal
岳父	*n.*	yuèfù	father-in-law
砸	*v.*	zá	pound, hit
早就		zǎojiù	as early as
枣	*n.*	zǎo	jujube
占领	*v.*	zhànlǐng	capture, occupy
中	*v.*	zhòng	hit
装作	*v.*	zhuāngzuò	disguise, pretend
追究	*v.*	zhuījiū	investigate, look into
捉弄	*v.*	zhuōnòng	make a fool of sb.
自首	*v.*	zìshǒu	give oneself up (to the police, authority, etc.)
罪名	*n.*	zuìmíng	charge, accusation
做客	*v.*	zuòkè	be a guest

项目策划：刘小琳　韩　颖
责任编辑：刘小琳
英文编辑：薛彧威
英文审定：龚燕灵　James Hutchison
插图绘制：硕果儿
设计指导：isles studio
设计制作：isles studio

图书在版编目（CIP）数据

水浒传 /（明）施耐庵原著；马娴，李梓萌改编 .— 北
京：华语教学出版社，2017
（"彩虹桥"汉语分级读物 . 6 级：2500 词）
ISBN 978-7-5138-1322-8

Ⅰ．①水… Ⅱ．①施… ②马… ③李… Ⅲ．①汉语—
对外汉语教学—语言读物 Ⅳ．① H195.5

中国版本图书馆 CIP 数据核字（2016）第 323816 号

水浒传

[明] 施耐庵　原著

马娴　李梓萌　改编

薛彧威　翻译

*

©华语教学出版社有限责任公司
华语教学出版社有限责任公司出版
（中国北京百万庄大街24号　邮政编码 100037）
电话：(86)10-68320585　68997826
传真：(86)10-68997826　68326333
网址：www.sinolingua.com.cn
电子信箱：hyjx@sinolingua.com.cn
新浪微博地址：http://weibo.com/sinolinguavip
北京京华虎彩印刷有限公司印刷
2017 年（32 开）第 1 版
2020 年第 1 版第 2 次印刷
（汉英）
ISBN 978-7-5138-1322-8
004900